QUICK MENTAL MATHS

MENTAL RECALL PRACTICE FOR 10 YEAR OLDS

SCHOLASTIC MATHS SKILLS

D0314194

AUTHOR
William Hartley

EDITOR
Kate Pearce

ASSISTANT EDITOR
Claire Miller

SERIES DESIGNER
Anna Oliwa

DESIGNER
Claire Belcher

ILLUSTRATIONS
Garry Davies

COVER ARTWORK
James Alexander/
David Oliver
(Berkeley
Studios)

Text © 1999 William Hartley
© 1999 Scholastic Ltd

Designed using Adobe Pagemaker
Published by Scholastic Ltd, Villiers House, Clarendon
Avenue, Leamington Spa, Warwickshire CV32 5PR

1234567890   8901234567

British Library Cataloguing-in-Publication Data
A catalogue record for this book is available from the
British Library.

ISBN 0-590-53922-1

SEC	SHEET	SHEET HEADING	SUGGESTED ORAL MATHS INPUT
COUNTING AND ORDERING	A1	COUNTING IN STEPS (INC NEGATIVE NUMBERS)	Count on/back in whole, fractional and decimal steps.
	A2	PLACE VALUE	Practise place value with six-digit numbers. See B11 and C11.
	A3	ORDERING WHOLE, FRACTIONAL AND % AMOUNTS	Order/compare whole, fractional, decimal and % amounts.
	A4	ESTIMATING AND APPROXIMATING	Estimate halves, quarters, and so on, of six-digit numbers.
	A5	ROUNDING WHOLE NUMBERS AND DECIMALS	Rounding six-digit numbers to the nearest 10/100/1000.
	A6	TEST YOUR SKILLS 1 (A1–A3 REVIEW SHEET)	As for A1–A3.
	A7	TEST YOUR SKILLS 2 (A4–A5 REVIEW SHEET)	As for A4 and A5.
ADDITION AND SUBTRACTION	B1	ADDITION FACTS	Practice with number pairs that total 100.
	B2	SUBTRACTION FACTS	Facts for numbers up to 20 and multiples of 10/100/1000.
	B3	RELATIONSHIP BETWEEN + AND –	36 + 14 = 50. What are the three other related facts?
	B4	PAIRS AND DOUBLES	Practise doubles of whole numbers from 1 to 50.
	B5	ADDING ORDER	Several numbers (some bridging). Start with the largest.
	B6	IDENTIFYING NEAR DOUBLES AND TREBLES	700 + 600 = double 700 – 100 or double 600 + 100.
	B7	CALCULATION PATTERNS (+ AND –)	410 + 8 = 418, 410 + 18 = 428, 410 + 28 = 438, and so on.
	B8	PARTITIONING AND RECOMBINING	Partition into 100s, 10s and 1s and add the 100s first.
	B9	BRIDGING AND ADJUSTING	Practise problems such as: 54 + 89 = 54 + 90 – 1 = 143, and so on.
	B10	+/– WHOLE, FRACTIONAL, DECIMAL & % AMOUNTS	+ and – whole, fractional, decimal and % amounts.
	B11	PLACE VALUE WHEN ADDING AND SUBTRACTING	+ and – whole numbers and decimals. See A2 and C11.
	B12	ADDING AND SUBTRACTING SEVERAL NUMBERS	Adding and subtracting several numbers with bridging.
	B13	TEST YOUR SKILLS 1 (B1–B6 REVIEW SHEET)	As for B1–B6.
	B14	TEST YOUR SKILLS 2 (B7–B12 REVIEW SHEET)	As for B7–B12.
MULTIPLICATION AND DIVISION	C1	MULTIPLICATION FACTS	Practise multiplication facts up to 10 × 10, consolidate ×7 and ×9.
	C2	DIVISION FACTS	Practise division facts up to 100 ÷ 10.
	C3	RELATIONSHIP BETWEEN × AND ÷	Practise breaking numbers into sub-sets (× and ÷).
	C4	DOUBLES, HALVES, QUARTERS AND EIGHTHS	Practise ways of finding different fractional amounts.
	C5	PARTITIONING WHEN MULTIPLYING	Multiplying hundreds first when multiplying HTU by U.
	C6	DIVISION WITH REMAINDERS	Divide HTU by 2 to 10. Convert remainders into fractions.
	C7	CALCULATION PATTERNS (× AND ÷)	Look for × and ÷ patterns in the 2 to 10 times tables.
	C8	FACTORS AND MULTIPLYING BY 10, 100, 1000	Factor games and decimal place shifting activities.
	C9	DIVIDING BY 10, 100, 1000	Division questions that involve decimal place shifting.
	C10	USING RELATED × AND ÷ FACTS	Give four facts for the numbers 7, 8 and 56.
	C11	PLACE VALUE WHEN MULTIPLYING AND DIVIDING	THTU problems. × and ÷ to two decimal places. See A2 and B11.
	C12	×/÷ WHOLE, FRACTIONAL, DECIMAL & % AMOUNTS	Practise ×/÷ facts for tables 2–10. ×/÷ fractions and decimals.
	C13	TEST YOUR SKILLS 1 (C1–C6 REVIEW SHEET)	As for C1–C6.
	C14	TEST YOUR SKILLS 2 (C7–C12 REVIEW SHEET)	As for C7–C12.
MULTISTEP AND MIXED OPERATIONS	D1	THE FOUR RULES OF NUMBER	Choose any relevant activity.
	D2	THE FOUR RULES OF NUMBER	Choose any relevant activity.
	D3	THE FOUR RULES OF NUMBER	Choose any relevant activity.
	D4	THE FOUR RULES OF NUMBER	Choose any relevant activity.

ABOUT THE SERIES

Quick Mental Maths aims to help children develop quick mental recall strategies – both the instant recall of known facts and speedy methods of figuring out 'unknowns'. Number facts are the vital building blocks for calculation, and their easy access is the key to efficient, accurate and confident mental mathematical ability.

Quick Mental Maths is a series of six photocopiable books providing a mixture of problem-posing styles of mental number practice for children aged 6 to 11. The level of ability at which each book is pitched has been broadly determined from the recommendations of the National Numeracy *Framework* document. *Quick Mental Maths* can be used as an independent resource in its own right to support any of the UK curriculum documentation, but can also be used in conjunction with the other Scholastic series *Developing Mental Maths* and *Practising Mental Maths*.

The books will provide valuable reinforcement of number bonds and times tables and help to improve the children's mental agility, as well as consolidating and extending their knowledge and use of mathematical vocabulary. These worksheets could be used as regular number practice – perhaps with a short time allowed each day for the children to complete one or more sections of a worksheet – as pre-SATs reinforcement/assessment tasks, or as worthwhile homework pages. All photocopiable sheets are indicated by the icon ⓟ.

ABOUT THE BOOK STRUCTURE
IN-BUILT DIFFERENTIATION

Each of the six books in this series addresses the same mental maths content under the same worksheet heading in each book, but at an increasing level of complexity. Thus, for example, you will find that worksheet A2 is always 'Place value' and worksheet C6 is always about 'Division with remainders'. Therefore, differentiation in a mixed-ability class is made easy by using the same worksheet number from more than one book to provide the same material at different levels.

YOUR INPUT

In order to reinforce the intended strategy to be used by the children to complete each sheet, it is recommended that you engage in some oral maths work with the class before they start. A varied use of mathematical vocabulary is very important when doing this. Some brief guidance for this aspect of your lesson preparation is given alongside each worksheet heading on the 'Teacher's information chart' on the opposite page. (You will find other suitable oral maths activities described in detail in the Scholastic teachers' book *Developing Mental Maths with 9–11 year olds*.)

RECORD-KEEPING

The photocopiable record sheet on the next page is to facilitate your record-keeping and assessment. This can either be given to the child as a record of his or her achievement or used as a teacher's record of which pages have been completed by which children and with what degree of success.

CONTENT ORGANIZATION

Each book is split into four sections:
A Counting and ordering
B Addition and subtraction
C Multiplication and division
D Multistep and mixed operations

The activities on each worksheet in sections A–C concentrate on one strategy, offering instant recall practice, number and word problems and a more investigational extension activity. The intention is that the page represents an 'achievable minimum' for children working at that level and that the extension activity (indicated by the icon 📖) will only be attempted by the more able child using a separate maths book or blank paper which can then be included in his or her personal maths file. In this way, it is hoped that the less able child will be able to tackle the majority of the page, while the more able child also has a 'special challenge'.

At the end of each of the first three sections (A–C) you will find two review tests relating specifically to the content of the sheets in that section. The problems are numbered to key in with the worksheet pages to which the questions relate. These review sheets will provide you with an opportunity to assess how well each child is progressing with the strategies on the worksheets in that section.

The final section of worksheets (D) gives the children the chance to practise some of their developing skills using more involved mental operation sequences that often require them to hold on to an interim number. The sheets in this section will really challenge the children.

ANSWERS

The final pages of the book provide the answers to all, but the most open-ended, of the questions on each worksheet. Answers in bold indicate those numbers which are given on the worksheets.

ABOUT THIS BOOK

Quick Mental Maths for 10 year olds is intended for Year 5/P6 children working at NC/NIC Level 3/4 (NNP Year 5) or confidently within Scottish Level C/D.

It is hoped the activities in this book will help to extend the children's understanding of the number system to hundreds of thousands and two decimal places, and that it will lead children to develop the many different strategies available to them for numbers with more digits, where the value of quick recall is so much more apparent.

RECORD SHEET

SHEET NO	MARK	COMMENT
A1		
A2		
A3		
A4		
A5		
A6		
A7		
B1		
B2		
B3		
B4		
B5		
B6		
B7		
B8		
B9		
B10		
B11		
B12		
B13		
B14		

SHEET NO	MARK	COMMENT
C1		
C2		
C3		
C4		
C5		
C6		
C7		
C8		
C9		
C10		
C11		
C12		
C13		
C14		
D1		
D2		
D3		
D4		

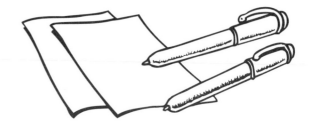

COUNTING IN STEPS (INC NEGATIVE NUMBERS)

A1

1. Fill in the missing numbers in these sequences.

a.
| 13 | → | | | 37 | 45 | | | | 77 |

b.
| | → | – 9 | | | | | 36 | 45 | |

c.
| 12.2 | → | 12.8 | | | | 15.2 | | | 17 |

2. Count back in 10s from the number at the start of the line until you reach the number at the end.

a. 1025 _____ 935

b. 21017 _____ 20 937

Count forward in 100s from the number at the start of the line until you reach the number at the end.

c. 5756 _____ 6656

d. 45 409 _____ 46 209

3. Starting at number 4, count on in steps of 7 and shade in the numbers you land on.

a.
1	2	3	4	5	6	7	8
9	10	11	12	13	14	15	16
17	18	19	20	21	22	23	24
25	26	27	28	29	30	13	32
33	34	35	36	37	38	39	40
41	42	43	44	45	46	47	48
49	50	51	52	53	54	55	56
57	58	59	60	61	62	63	64

Continue counting in 7s and write down the next seven numbers in the sequence.

b. _____

Predict the next three amounts in these sequences and write them down.

c. $1\frac{1}{2}$ $2\frac{3}{4}$ 4 _____

d. 15 $13\frac{1}{2}$ 12 _____

Starting at 999 count forward for eight steps and then back for eight steps in these amounts: 15, 105, 3.2 and $4\frac{1}{2}$. Make up some number sequences using your own rules. Can your friend guess the rule?

PLACE VALUE

1. Write these amounts in figures.

a. forty-three _____

b. two hundred and
seventy-eight _____

c. five thousand, nine
hundred and sixty-one _____

d. twenty-one thousand,
six hundred and
eighty-three _____

e. four hundred and fifty-seven
thousand, nine hundred
and thirty-two _____

f. six hundred and eight _____

g. seven thousand and
nineteen _____

h. five thousand and six _____

i. three thousand eight
hundred _____

j. ten thousand and two _____

k. eighty thousand and
eighty-eight _____

l. eighty-eight thousand
and eight _____

2. Write these amounts in words.

a. 105 _____

b. 150 _____

c. 8006 _____

d. 8060 _____

e. 8600 _____

f. 6008 _____

g. 24 970 _____

_____

What does each digit in 472 935 represent?

h. 4 = _____   5 = _____

2 = _____   9 = _____

3 = _____   7 = _____

3. Write the decimal fractions for these amounts.

a. $\frac{1}{2}$ ___ $\frac{2}{8}$ ___ $\frac{27}{100}$ ___ $\frac{3}{6}$ ___ $\frac{4}{5}$ ___

b. $\frac{1}{4}$ ___ $\frac{5}{10}$ ___ $\frac{4}{8}$ ___ $\frac{6}{8}$ ___ $\frac{1}{5}$ ___

c. $\frac{3}{10}$ ___ $\frac{7}{10}$ ___ $\frac{9}{10}$ ___ $\frac{2}{5}$ ___ $\frac{3}{4}$ ___

Using decimal notation, write down the tenths from 0.1 to 10 like this: 0.1, 0.2, 0.3...
and so on. Now start at 100 and write down the hundredths counting back to 99 like
this: 100, 99.99, 99.98...

QUICK MENTAL MATHS

ORDERING WHOLE, FRACTIONAL AND % AMOUNTS

1. In the boxes, write either a four or five-digit number to complete these number sentences.

a. £3162 < [ ]

b. £49 074 > [ ]

c. £1030 > [ ]

d. £58 000 < [ ]

e. £2653 < [ ]

Choose a suitable fraction to complete these number sentences.

f. $\frac{3}{5}$ > [ ]

g. $\frac{3}{4}$ < [ ]

h. $\frac{2}{3}$ < [ ]

i. $\frac{7}{10}$ > [ ]

j. $\frac{5}{8}$ > [ ]

In the boxes, write an appropriate decimal fraction to 1 or 2 decimal places.

k. 43.2cm > [ ]

l. 59.95km > [ ]

m. 69.9kg < [ ]

n. 8.57mm < [ ]

o. 0.65ml > [ ]

2. Arrange these numbers by size, starting with the largest.

a. 94 783   83 947   97 834   84 793   83 497   93 478   83 794   98 347

Arrange these numbers by size, starting with the smallest.

b. 101   − 83   100   83   − 79   110   79   − 100   1   1100   − 1

Circle the largest amount in each pair of numbers.

c. $\frac{2}{3}$ d. $\frac{3}{6}$ e. $\frac{7}{10}$ f. $\frac{1}{4}$ g. 0.1   h. $\frac{1}{2}$

0.2   0.8   0.75   0.14   0.16   0.25

3. Work out the answers to these problems.

a. $\frac{7}{10}$ = ___%   b. $\frac{4}{10}$ = ___%   c. $\frac{1}{4}$ = ___%   d. $\frac{1}{2}$ = ___%   e. $\frac{3}{4}$ = ___%

Write out all the numbers that will divide into 100 exactly. Write these numbers as a % of 200. Three of the numbers will have to be written as decimal fractions.

QUICK MENTAL MATHS

ESTIMATING AND APPROXIMATING

1. From the list, choose the amount that is nearest to the actual answer to each problem and write it in the first box. Write the correct answer in the second box.

550   5500   160   100   2500   175   900   125   350   75

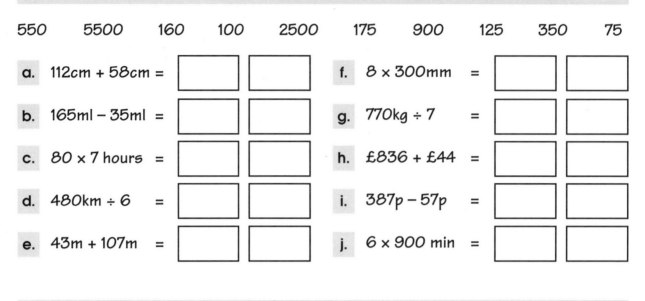

a. 112cm + 58cm =

b. 165ml − 35ml =

c. 80 × 7 hours =

d. 480km ÷ 6 =

e. 43m + 107m =

f. 8 × 300mm =

g. 770kg ÷ 7 =

h. £836 + £44 =

i. 387p − 57p =

j. 6 × 900 min =

2. Estimate the numbers marked by the arrows on these number lines.

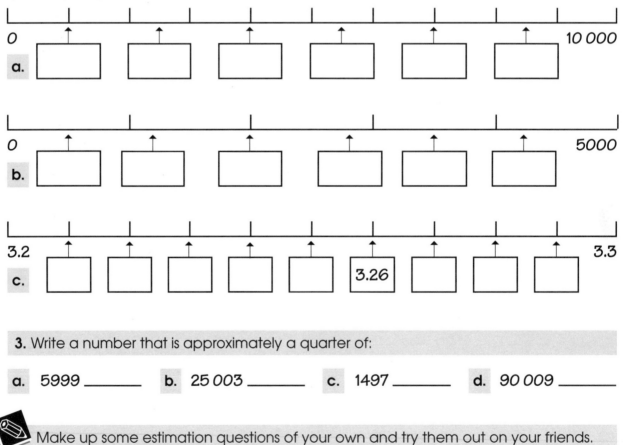

a. 0 .... 10 000

b. 0 5000

c. 3.2 .... 3.3 (3.26)

3. Write a number that is approximately a quarter of:

a. 5999 _____   **b.** 25 003 _____   **c.** 1497 _____   **d.** 90 009 _____

Make up some estimation questions of your own and try them out on your friends. You could ask questions such as: How many words on the page of a book? How many leaves on a plant?

QUICK MENTAL MATHS

ROUNDING WHOLE NUMBERS AND DECIMALS

1. Round these amounts to the nearest:

a. 10 metres.	**b.** 100 kilometres.	**c.** 1000 miles
46m _____	749km _____	501 miles _____
1008m _____	3950km _____	26 750 miles _____
553m _____	48 351km _____	7240 miles _____
29 635m _____	679 899km _____	39 202 miles _____

2. In column X write the answer to each number sentence. In column Y write the answer rounded to the nearest 10.

						X	Y
a.	120	+	36	=			
b.	170	−	58	=			
c.	6	×	8	=			
d.	84	÷	6	=			
e.	98	÷	2	=			
f.	65	−	20	=			

						X	Y
g.	13	+	28	=			
h.	9	×	9	=			
i.	150	−	32	=			
j.	64	+	90	=			
k.	300	÷	4	=			
l.	14	×	3	=			

3. Round these decimals to the nearest whole number.

a. 3.4 _____ 97.8 _____ 109.1 _____

b. 6.6 _____ 45.9 _____ 316.3 _____

c. 8.3 _____ 38.1 _____ 272.5 _____

d. 4.6 _____ 21.7 _____ 520.9 _____

e. What is £4.87 to the nearest 10p?

_____

f. What is 3.34m to the nearest 10cm?

_____

Make a list of six items and price each item in pounds and pence. None of the prices should be a multiple of 10. Work out the total cost of the items and then their total cost to the nearest £.

QUICK MENTAL MATHS

TEST YOUR SKILLS 1 (A1–A3)

A1 Fill in the missing numbers in these sequences.

a.	1		27	40				

b.		135		105	90			

c.			15.7		17.3	18.1		

d.	−16		−2	5				

e.				8.07		7.95	7.89	

f.	$24\frac{1}{2}$						$3\frac{1}{2}$	0

A2 Write one number that includes all the following amounts.

a. 8 hundredths   3 tens   1 hundred

   426 thousands   7 tenths   5 ones

What does each digit in 596 243 represent?

b. 5 = _____   6 = _____   4 = _____

   3 = _____   2 = _____   9 = _____

Write the decimal fractions for these amounts.

c. $\frac{4}{10}$ _____   three fifths _____ $\frac{1}{4}$ _____   six eighths _____

A3 Order these sets of amounts according to their size, starting with the smallest.

97 °C		£43 709		25%	
− 98 °C		£43 790		0.18	
78 °C		£43 897		$\frac{3}{4}$	
49 °C		£43 907		0.7	
− 49 °C		£43 987		50%	
− 79 °C		£43 970		$\frac{4}{5}$	

COUNTING AND ORDERING

TOTAL

TEST YOUR SKILLS 2 (A4–A5)

A4 From the list, choose the amount that is nearest to the actual answer to each problem and write it in the first box. Write the correct answer in the second box.

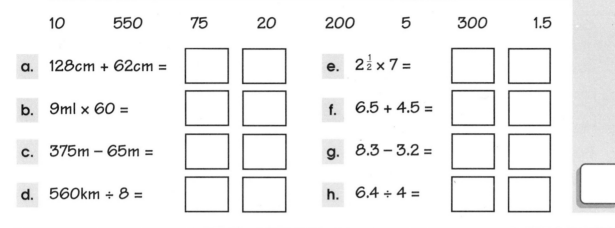

10	550	75	20	200	5	300	1.5

a. 128cm + 62cm = ☐ ☐

b. 9ml × 60 = ☐ ☐

c. 375m − 65m = ☐ ☐

d. 560km ÷ 8 = ☐ ☐

e. $2\frac{1}{2} \times 7 =$ ☐ ☐

f. 6.5 + 4.5 = ☐ ☐

g. 8.3 − 3.2 = ☐ ☐

h. 6.4 ÷ 4 = ☐ ☐

Estimate the numbers marked by the arrows on these number lines.

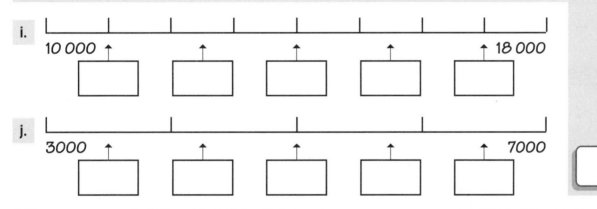

i. 10 000   18 000

j. 3000   7000

A5 Round these numbers to the nearest 10, 100 and 1000. The first one has been done for you.

a.	555	560	600	1000
b.	9783			
c.	4496			
d.	638			

e.	8572			
f.	3007			
g.	6926			
h.	7987			

Round these decimals to the nearest whole number.

i. 5.6 _____   2.4 _____   3.8 _____   6.2 _____   9.5 _____

j. 3.26 _____   8.51 _____   7.07 _____   42.3 _____   20.7 _____

TOTAL

COUNTING AND ORDERING

ADDITION FACTS

1. Work out the missing amounts in these addition sums.

a. £26 + £44 = [ ]

b. 450m + [ ] = 500m

c. [ ] + 19kg = 90kg.

d. 80mm + 920mm = [ ]

e. [ ] + 30km = 700km

f. 63cm + [ ] = 90cm

g. 350ml + 450ml = [ ]

h. 70g + [ ] = 300g

i. [ ] + £20 = £800

j. 225m + 475m = [ ]

k. [ ] + 900kg = 1400kg

l. 45mm + [ ] = 610mm

2. Find the total of each pair of numbers. Think carefully about the easiest way to do them.

a. 21, 79 _____   g. 49, 43 _____

b. 59, 33 _____   h. 42, 58 _____

c. 64, 36 _____   i. 51, 49 _____

d. 48, 42 _____   j. 46, 54 _____

e. 138, 162 _____   k. 24, 39 _____

f. 37, 44 _____   l. 173, 127 _____

Fill in the missing numbers in this addition table.

m.

+	500	800	200	600	300
100			300		
400					700
700	1200				
900				1500	

3. Solve the problems below.

a. What number is forty-four more than one hundred and fifty-six? _____

b. Increase two hundred and thirty-five by sixty-five. _____

c. Leon has two lengths of wood. One length measures 4m 25cm and the other length measures 3m 65cm. Write down the total length of the two pieces of wood, first in cm and then in m and cm.

_____ cm   _____ m   _____ cm

Draw an addition table like the one in part 2. Write the numbers 106, 407, 708 and 909 down the left-hand column and the numbers 509, 808, 207, 606 and 305 across the top. Fill in the table.

SUBTRACTION FACTS

1. Subtract the smaller number from the larger number in each pair. Think carefully about the easiest way of doing this.

a. 420, 370 _____   g. 800, 3487 _____

b. 270, 350 _____   h. 9621, 100 _____

c. 780, 490 _____   i. 500, 8112 _____

d. 490, 650 _____   j. 300, 6756 _____

e. 380, 560 _____   k. 7356, 700 _____

f. 870, 680 _____   l. 900, 5509 _____

Fill in the missing numbers in this subtraction table.

m.

–	856	684	963	775	562
230			733		
410					152
120				655	
340		344			

2. Work out the missing amounts in these subtraction problems.

a. 150ml – 40ml = ☐

b. 1200m – ☐ = 500m

c. ☐ – 80cm = 60cm

d. 1600km – 800km = ☐

e. ☐ – 60mm = 60mm

f. 1300cm – ☐ = 800cm

g. 1800m – 900m = ☐

h. £160 – ☐ = £70

i. ☐ – 600g = 800g

j. 190ml – 50ml = ☐

k. ☐ – 400km = 1100km

l. 110mm – ☐ 60mm

3. Solve the problems below. Write your answers in words.

a. Take nine hundred away from 1700.   _____

b. What number is added to 364 to make 900?   _____

c. By how many is 700 greater than 538?   _____

d. Find the difference between 352 and 170.   _____

e. From 486 subtract two hundred and forty.   _____

 Draw a subtraction table like the one in part 1. Add 200 to each of the numbers in the left-hand column and in the row across the top. Fill in the table.

RELATIONSHIP BETWEEN + AND –

1. Fill in the answers and then write out the set of number sentences. The first one has been done for you.

a. 146 + 28 = _____174_____   28 + 146 = 174   174 – 146 = 28   174 – 28 = 146

b. 107 – 43 = _____   _____

c. 56 + 224 = _____   _____

d. 685 – 27 = _____   _____

e. 758 + 49 = _____   _____

2. Join two numbers to each number box so that they make a correct addition sum. Write out the sum. Then change the numbers round in each sum to make two subtraction facts. One has been done for you.

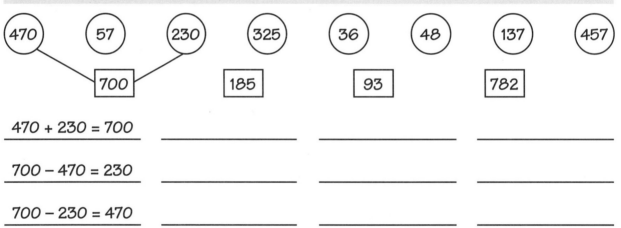

(470)   (57)   (230)   (325)   (36)   (48)   (137)   (457)

[700]   [185]   [93]   [782]

470 + 230 = 700   _____   _____   _____

700 – 470 = 230   _____   _____   _____

700 – 230 = 470   _____   _____   _____

3. In the right-hand box, write an addition fact using all three numbers from the left-hand box.

In the right-hand box, write a subtraction fact using all three numbers from the left-hand box.

a.

72, 252, 180	72 + 180 = 252
160, 53, 213	
320, 810, 490	
437, 370, 67	

b.

380, 870, 490	870 – 490 = 380
7389, 500, 6889	
900, 700, 1600	
325, 360, 685	

Using the numbers 316, 76, 260, 240 and 56, make up as many three number addition and subtraction statements as you can, for example, 316 – 260 = 56.

PAIRS AND DOUBLES

1. Next to each number write down the amount that needs to be added to it to make 50.

a. 24 _____   36 _____   48 _____   23 _____   18 _____   26 _____

b. 39 _____   25 _____   34 _____   12 _____   37 _____   27 _____

Now write the amount that needs to be added to these numbers to make 100.

c. 56 _____   73 _____   22 _____   6 _____   43 _____   17 _____

d. 61 _____   78 _____   64 _____   28 _____   49 _____   35 _____

2a. Answer using the £ sign.	**b.** Write the answers in metres.	**c.** Give the answers in pence.
260p + 390p = _____	910cm + 520cm = _____	£2.70 + £9.80 = _____
740p + 780p = _____	830cm + 320cm = _____	£8.70 + £4.40 = _____
490p + 560p = _____	310cm + 830cm = _____	£7.60 + £7.80 = _____
970p + 650p = _____	470cm + 680cm = _____	£9.50 + £6.50 = _____

3. Double the first number and then double that answer. The first one has been done for you.

a.

31	62	124
46		
17		
37		
24		
12		

b.

48		
27		
16		
42		
23		
35		

c.

39		
21		
49		
15		
28		
19		

d.

26		
13		
45		
18		
36		
14		

 List all the numbers from 51 to 100. Next to each number write down its double. Carry on past 100 if you have time.

QUICK MENTAL MATHS

ADDING ORDER

1. Rearrange these sums in your head so that you start with the largest amount. Look for number bonds.

a. 7 + 8 + 3 + 115 + 2 + 25 = _____

b. 4 + 3 + 14 + 7 + 6 + 506 = _____

c. 4 + 4 + 15 + 485 + 6 + 6 = _____

d. 22 + 1 + 748 + 9 + 3 + 7 = _____

e. 5 + 6 + 26 + 5 + 4 + 364 = _____

f. 1 + 7 + 19 + 121 + 3 + 9 = _____

g. _____ = 7 + 5 + 5 + 594 + 3 + 16

h. _____ = 13 + 2 + 1 + 8 + 9 + 727

i. _____ = 6 + 2 + 17 + 243 + 8 + 4

j. _____ = 7 + 359 + 5 + 11 + 3 + 5

k. _____ = 2 + 4 + 13 + 8 + 6 + 637

l. _____ = 9 + 8 + 1 + 856 + 2 + 24

2. Answer these questions. Remember the rule about putting the largest number first.

a. The masses of three different crayons are 55g, 65g and 70g.
Calculate the total mass of all three crayons. _____

b. Class 1 has seventeen children, Class 2 twenty-four children and Class 3 thirty-six children. Find the number of children in all three classes. _____

3. Write eight addition sums. Choose the numbers from this grid. Put the largest number first. Use a different set of three numbers for each sum. Now work out your sums.

_____

_____

_____

_____

10	65	11	100	35
15	80	20	30	55
33	85	90	95	66
44	110	75	99	40
45	5	77	25	88

_____

_____

_____

_____

Make up your own addition sums using four numbers. Use numbers that are two or three-digit multiples of 5. Remember to put the largest number first and to work out the answers in your head.

IDENTIFYING NEAR DOUBLES AND TREBLES

1. Add these near doubles. Look at the examples which are there to help you with your thinking.

300 + 290 = 590. This sum can be done quickly by saying double 300 minus 10.
450 + 455 = 905. This sum can be done quickly by saying double 450 plus 5.

a. 350 + 360 = ☐   **g.** 300 + 280 + 280 = ☐

b. 600 + 570 = ☐   **h.** 199 + 201 + 200 = ☐

c. 920 + 900 = ☐   **i.** 790 + 800 = ☐

d. 430 + 400 = ☐   **j.** 945 + 950 = ☐

e. 200 + 190 + 190 = ☐   **k.** 550 + 530 = ☐

f. 100 + 110 + 110 = ☐   **l.** 250 + 230 = ☐

2. Here are two other ways to think when adding near doubles. (There are other ways.)

690 + 680 = 700 + 700 − 10 − 20 = 1370
800 + 700 = 800 + 800 − 100 or 700 + 700 + 100 = 1500

Write out your *thinking process* when you do these sums.

a. £470 + £490 = _____

b. 610m + 620m = _____

c. 800g + 900g = _____

3. Look for doubles to help you answer these problems. Write your answers in words.

a. What number is eighty-eight more than ninety? _____

b. Find the total of 400, 414 and 420. _____

c. Add together sixty-seven, seventy-one and 69. _____

Add some four-digit numbers that are near doubles and write out your thinking in full. Like this: 4300 + 4295 = *4300 + 4300 − 5 = 8600 − 5 = 8595.*

B7

CALCULATION PATTERNS (+ AND –)

1. Do these calculations. Then look at your answers to help you answer the questions in part 2.

a. 29 + 35 = _____   7 + 83 = _____   251 + 5 = _____   37 + 37 = _____

b. 18 + 56 = _____   6 + 68 = _____   4 + 398 = _____   42 + 42 = _____

c. 37 – 29 = _____   45 – 9 = _____   413 – 7 = _____   67 – 25 = _____

d. 85 + 22 = _____   9 + 56 = _____   517 + 8 = _____   53 + 46 = _____

e. 34 + 37 = _____   4 + 67 = _____   6 + 609 = _____   28 + 71 = _____

f. 86 – 54 = _____   72 – 8 = _____   742 – 4 = _____   96 – 48 = _____

g. 6 + 12 + 142 = _____   234 + 8 + 16 = _____   14 + 356 + 4 = _____

h. 5 + 17 + 443 = _____   521 + 9 + 23 = _____   39 + 603 + 1 = _____

2. What kind of number do you get if you add:

a. three EVEN numbers? _____   **e.** an EVEN number to an ODD number?

b. two ODD numbers? _____   _____

c. three ODD numbers? _____   **f.** an ODD number to an EVEN number?

d. two EVEN numbers? _____   _____

What kind of number do you get if you subtract:

g. two ODD numbers? _____   **h.** two EVEN numbers? _____

3. Do these problems. Can you see the pattern. Tell your teacher what you find.

a. 126 + 9 = _____   126 + 19 = _____   126 + 29 = _____   126 + 39 = _____

b. 147 – _____ = 139   147 – _____ = 129   147 – _____ = 119   147 – _____ = 109

The answers to part 2 provide you with some facts about ODD and EVEN numbers. See if you can find out any more ODD and EVEN facts. Write them down and test them out.

QUICK MENTAL MATHS

ADDITION AND SUBTRACTION

PARTITIONING AND RECOMBINING

1. The sum below shows the *thinking stages* for finding the right answer.

$$234 + 48 = 230 + 40 \text{ plus } 4 + 8 = 270 + 12 = 282$$

Do these two calculations. Write out your *thinking stages* in the same way as the example above.

a. 558 + 46 = _____

b. 37 + 755 = _____

Look at this calculation. Do the first sum in the same way and try to *think* like that for the others.

$$427 + 49 = 427 + 3 + 46 = 430 + 46 = 476$$

c. 642 + 29 = _____

d. 876 + 37 = _____   257 + 28 = _____   385 + 46 = _____

2. Look at the completed grid below. Read it from left to right and top to bottom as you would a book. Now fill in the other two grids in the same way to find the answers.

	624	+	355		
=	600	+	300		
+	20	+	50		
+	4	+	5		
=	900	+	70	+	9
=	979				

	434	+	242		
=		+			
+		+			
+		+			
=		+		+	
=					

			+		
=	200	+			
+		+	20		
+	4	+			
=		+		+	
=	959				

3. Use any of the *thinking stages* shown above to work out the answers to these problems. To help your memory, write down the answer to each stage as you go along.

a. Find the sum of 624 and seventy-five. _____

b. Total up forty-eight and five hundred and fifty-six. _____

Draw some grids like those in part 2. Write some pairs of three-digit numbers along the top row, then fill in the missing numbers. Try using four-digit numbers. You will need an extra row of boxes.

BRIDGING AND ADJUSTING

1. The two examples below show the *thinking stages* for finding the correct answer.

$$64 + 79 = 143 \qquad \text{Work this out as } 64 + 80 - 1 = 143$$
$$138 - 47 = 91 \qquad \text{Work this out as } 138 - 50 + 3 = 91$$

Do these sums in the same way, showing your *thinking stages*.

a. $62 + 56 =$ _____

b. $94 + 87 =$ _____

c. $83 + 78 =$ _____

d. $82 + 99 =$ _____

2. Here are other ways of thinking when adding and subtracting.

$$137 + 39 = 137 + 40 - 1 = 176 \qquad\qquad 137 + 41 = 137 + 40 + 1 = 178$$
$$187 - 21 = 187 - 20 - 1 = 166 \qquad\qquad 187 - 19 = 187 - 20 + 1 = 168$$

Now do these problems in the same way, showing your thinking stages.

a.	157	+	19	=	$157 + 20 - 1$	=	176
b.	385	–	69	=		=	
c.	537	+	41	=		=	
d.	542	–	21	=		=	
e.	246	+	39	=		=	

3. Solve this problem using one of the strategies suggested on this page.

A jar contained 454g of marmalade. Seventy-nine grams of
marmalade were eaten. What mass still remained in the jar? _____

 Make up five addition and five subtraction problems similar to those in part 2 but
using three numbers. Your problems should look something like this:
$438 + 39 + 59 = (438 + 40 + 60) - 2 = 536.$

QUICK MENTAL MATHS

+ AND – WHOLE, FRACTIONAL, DECIMAL AND % AMOUNTS

1. Work out the answers to these problems. Think carefully about which strategy you are going to use.

a. £370.00 + £250.00 = _____

b. 920km take away 480km = _____

c. 3687 miles – 800 miles = _____

d. 900kg + 726kg = _____

e. 740g minus 360g = _____

f. 982 litres + 600 litres = _____

g. From 3000m take away four hundred and seven hundred metres. _____

h. A train travels 700km, 400km and 900km. How far is that? _____

i. 793kg subtract 250kg = _____

j. 139 miles + 860 miles = _____

k. £180 add £460 = _____

l. 328 litres – 190 litres = _____

m. 1753km – 900km = _____

n. Total up 438g and 513g _____

2. Fill in the missing fractions, decimals and percentages in these charts.

$\frac{1}{2}$	0.5	50%
$\frac{3}{5}$		
	0.17	
		70%

		1%
	0.49	
$\frac{4}{5}$		
	0.25	

	0.9	
$\frac{3}{4}$		
		91%
		40%

		10%
		9%
	0.2	
$\frac{3}{10}$		

3. Think carefully as you answer these questions about fractions. How many:

a. quarters in two halves? _____

b. eighths in a half? _____

c. halves in four eighths? _____

d. quarters in a whole one? _____

e. eighths in three quarters? _____

f. quarters in a half? _____

g. halves in a whole one? _____

h. quarters in six eighths? _____

i. eighths in two halves? _____

j. eighths in two quarters? _____

Find 25% and 75% of these amounts: 200, 500, 1000, 1120, 2600 and 3760.

B11

PLACE VALUE WHEN ADDING AND SUBTRACTING

1. Match the answer to each problem with the same amount in words. The first one has been done for you.

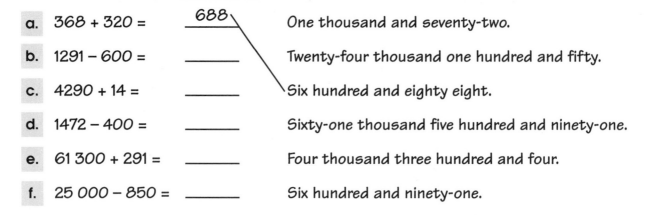

a. 368 + 320 =   _688_   One thousand and seventy-two.

b. 1291 – 600 =   _____   Twenty-four thousand one hundred and fifty.

c. 4290 + 14 =   _____   Six hundred and eighty eight.

d. 1472 – 400 =   _____   Sixty-one thousand five hundred and ninety-one.

e. 61 300 + 291 =   _____   Four thousand three hundred and four.

f. 25 000 – 850 =   _____   Six hundred and ninety-one.

2. Write down the answer in the first box. In the second box, give the value of the 7 in the answer.

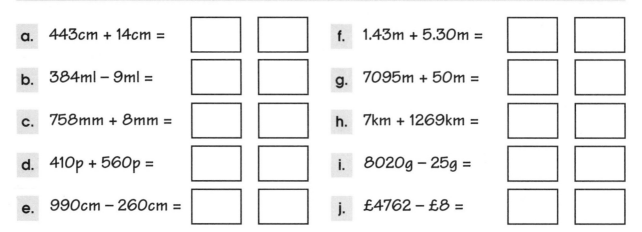

a. 443cm + 14cm =

b. 384ml – 9ml =

c. 758mm + 8mm =

d. 410p + 560p =

e. 990cm – 260cm =

f. 1.43m + 5.30m =

g. 7095m + 50m =

h. 7km + 1269km =

i. 8020g – 25g =

j. £4762 – £8 =

3. Give the answers to the following problems in figures.

a. How many tens in three hundred and eighty-seven?   _____

b. How many thousands in twenty-four thousand and fifty-six?   _____

c. Which is less: five thousand two hundred or 53 hundreds?   _____

d. Which is more: twenty hundreds or 2002 thousands?   _____

e. Write the number that is equivalent to: fifty-two thousands, four hundreds, nine tens and three ones.   _____

Use the digits 3, 4, 5, 6 and 7 and see how many five-digit numbers of different values you can write. Do the same with 1, 2, 8, 9 and 0. If you have time, try other groups of five digits.

P

QUICK MENTAL MATHS

NAME _____   CLASS _____

ADDING AND SUBTRACTING SEVERAL NUMBERS

B12

1. Add together these numbers. Each time, look for pairs that make 10 or 100.

a. 10 + 70 + 90 + 30 = _____

b. 80 + 90 + 20 + 50 = _____

c. 70 + 30 + 60 + 90 = _____

d. 20 + 80 + 3 + 40 + 7 + 60 = _____

e. 80 + 4 + 90 + 6 + 50 + 50 = _____

f. 60 + 23 + 7 + 40 + 6 + 70 = _____

Subtract any two numbers in the left-hand column from the numbers at the top.

g.

−	800	650	900	570	200	450	300	250	500
60		60				60			
90		90							90
80						80			80
		500				310			330

2. Solve these addition and subtraction problems.

a. Find the sum of 30cm, 80cm and 1m 60cm and give the answer in cm. _____

b. Subtract 320km and 10km from 679 kilometres. _____

c. To thirty-six add three, five, nine and six. _____

d. When 20 and 120 are taken away from 856 how many are left? _____

e. From one hundred and fifty-eight remove seven, five, two and nine. _____

3. Fill in the missing numbers in the calculations below. Look for number bonds.

a. 45 + 25 + 7 + 13 = _____

b. _____ + 14 + 18 + 12 = 50

c. 29 + _____ + 21 + 9 = 83

d. 38 + 3 + _____ +112 = 180

e. 95 − 15 − 8 − _____ = 50

f. 87 − 21 − 27 − 19 = _____

Draw a chart like the one in part 1. Write the numbers 150, 170 and 140 in the left-hand column. Make the numbers across the top larger by 1000. Now fill in the chart in the same way as before.

B13

TEST YOUR SKILLS 1 (B1–B6)

B1 Find the total of each pair of numbers. Think about the strategies you can use.

a. 40, 70 _____   e. 400, 800 _____   i. 830, 80 _____

b. 44, 56 _____   f. 235, 524 _____   j. 55, 145 _____

c. 27, 27 _____   g. 380, 380 _____   k. 640, 50 _____

d. 65, 28 _____   h. 605, 294 _____   l. 125, 85 _____

B2 Fill in these subtraction charts.

–	575	984	463	791
320				
450			13	

–	630	920	840	750
460				
590	40			

B3 Write out the four related addition and subtraction facts for each set of numbers.

a. 256   45   301   _____   _____

_____   _____

b. 800   480   1280   _____   _____

_____   _____

B4 What amount would you need to add to each number to make a) 50 and
b) 100? The first one has been done for you.

24 [26] [76]   17 [ ] [ ]   32 [ ] [ ]   46 [ ] [ ]

B5 Make up four addition sums using the numbers in the grid. Use two numbers
in each sum. You can only use each number once. Put the largest amount
first each time. Then work out your sums.

_____

25	63	38	14
41	60	76	59

_____

_____

B6 400 + 385 = *double 400 minus 15* = 785. Do the following sums in the same way.

500 + 499 = _____   787 + 800 = _____

TOTAL

P

QUICK MENTAL MATHS

TEST YOUR SKILLS 2 (B7–B12)

B7 Answer these questions by writing 'odd' or 'even' next to them.
What kind of number do you get if you:

a. add three ODD numbers? _____

b. add two EVEN numbers? _____

c. add an ODD and EVEN number? _____

d. subtract an ODD and EVEN number? _____

e. add three EVEN numbers? _____

f. add two ODD numbers? _____

g. add an EVEN and ODD number? _____

h. subtract two EVEN numbers? _____

i. subtract two ODD numbers? _____

B8 Fill in the missing numbers in the thinking stages of this sum.

457 + 42 = 450 + _____ + 7 + 2 = _____ + 9 = _____

B9 Write down your thinking stages as you do these calculations.

a. 93 + 68 = _____

b. 72 + 89 = _____

c. 64 + 57 = _____

d. 428 – 58 = _____

e. 249 – 86 = _____

f. 337 – 47 = _____

B10 Fill in the missing fractions, decimals and percentages (%) in these charts.

a.

$\frac{1}{100}$		

b.

		10%

c.

	0.2	

d.

	0.25	

e.

$\frac{1}{2}$		

f.

		75%

g. 820km – 380km = _____

h. 800kg + 942kg = _____

B11 Write down in the spaces the value of each digit in the number shown.

473 956   4 = _____   7 = _____   3 = _____

9 = _____   5 = _____   6 = _____

B12 Complete the calculations written below. Look for number bonds.

a. 80 – 15 – 8 – 22 – 9 = _____

b. 36 + 7 + 24 + 3 + 15 = _____

TOTAL

ADDITION AND SUBTRACTION

MULTIPLICATION FACTS

1. Work out the missing amounts in these multiplication problems.

a. £8 × 6 = ☐

b. 9m × ☐ = 63m

c. ☐ × 5kg = 45kg

d. 10mm × 8 = ☐

e. ☐ × 9km = 45km

f. 6cm × ☐ = 42cm

g. 7ml × 10 = ☐

h. 11g × ☐ = 77g

i. ☐ × £5 = £30

j. 7m × 7 = ☐

k. ☐ × 9kg = 63kg

l. 7mm × ☐ = 42mm

2. Find the product of each of these pairs of numbers.

a. 8, 7 ____   8, 8 ____   3, 7 ____

b. 4, 5 ____   5, 6 ____   9, 8 ____

c. 10, 9 ____   7, 5 ____   6, 9 ____

d. 6, 8 ____   9, 9 ____   4, 6 ____

e. 4, 9 ____   10, 7 ____   6, 10 ____

f. 9, 6 ____   6, 6 ____   7, 8 ____

Fill in the missing amounts in this table.

g.

×	11p	14p	12p	15p	13p
5					65p
3	33p			45p	
6			72p		
4		56p			

3. Solve the problems below.

a. What is the product of fifteen and five? _____

b. A bottle of lemonade makes seven drinks. How many drinks will twelve bottles make? _____

c. What number is thirteen times more than six? _____

d. An eighth of my money is twelve pence. What is my total amount? _____

✏ Start at 1 × 15 = 15 and write out the 15 times table. See if you can get as far as 20 × 15 or even further. If you have time, do the same with other 'teens' tables.

QUICK MENTAL MATHS

DIVISION FACTS

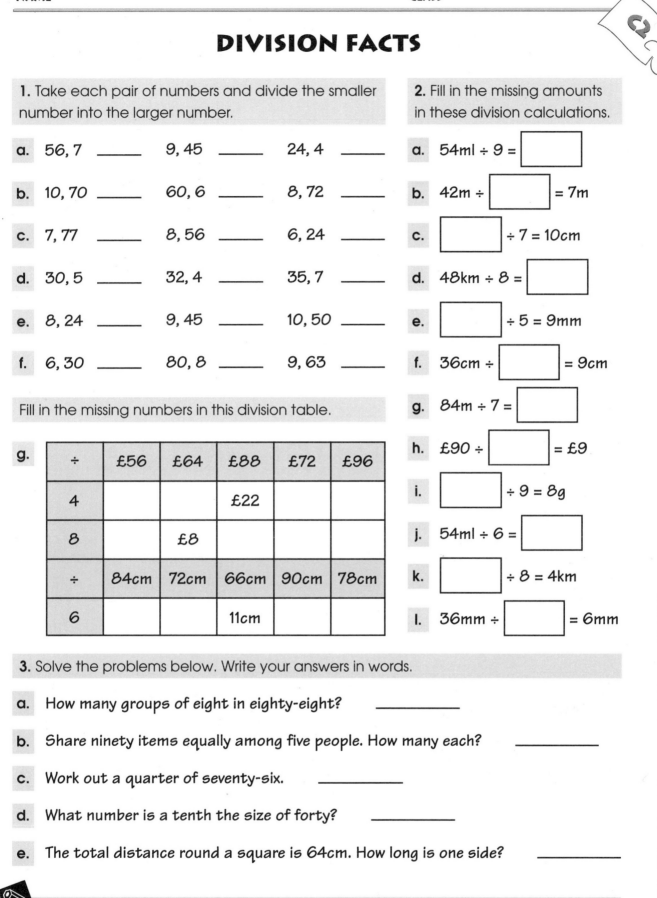

1. Take each pair of numbers and divide the smaller number into the larger number.

a. 56, 7 _____   9, 45 _____   24, 4 _____

b. 10, 70 _____   60, 6 _____   8, 72 _____

c. 7, 77 _____   8, 56 _____   6, 24 _____

d. 30, 5 _____   32, 4 _____   35, 7 _____

e. 8, 24 _____   9, 45 _____   10, 50 _____

f. 6, 30 _____   80, 8 _____   9, 63 _____

Fill in the missing numbers in this division table.

g.

÷	£56	£64	£88	£72	£96
4			£22		
8		£8			

÷	84cm	72cm	66cm	90cm	78cm
6			11cm		

2. Fill in the missing amounts in these division calculations.

a. $54ml \div 9 = $ ☐

b. $42m \div$ ☐ $= 7m$

c. ☐ $\div 7 = 10cm$

d. $48km \div 8 = $ ☐

e. ☐ $\div 5 = 9mm$

f. $36cm \div$ ☐ $= 9cm$

g. $84m \div 7 = $ ☐

h. $£90 \div$ ☐ $= £9$

i. ☐ $\div 9 = 8g$

j. $54ml \div 6 = $ ☐

k. ☐ $\div 8 = 4km$

l. $36mm \div$ ☐ $= 6mm$

3. Solve the problems below. Write your answers in words.

a. How many groups of eight in eighty-eight? _____

b. Share ninety items equally among five people. How many each? _____

c. Work out a quarter of seventy-six. _____

d. What number is a tenth the size of forty? _____

e. The total distance round a square is 64cm. How long is one side? _____

Start at $15 \div 15 = 1$, $30 \div 15 = 2$... and see how far you can get. Can you reach $300 \div 15 = 20$?

RELATIONSHIP BETWEEN × AND ÷

1. Fill in the answers and then write out the set of number sentences in the same way as the first one has been done.

a. $9 \times 8 = \underline{\quad 72 \quad}$ $8 \times 9 = 72$ $72 \div 9 = 8$ $72 \div 8 = 9$

b. $7 \times 12 = \underline{\qquad}$ _____

c. $48 \div 6 = \underline{\qquad}$ _____

d. $54 \div 9 = \underline{\qquad}$ _____

e. $5 \times 14 = \underline{\qquad}$ _____

2. Join two numbers to each number box to make a division problem. Like this: $48 \div 8 = 6$. Write out the problem. Then change the numbers round in each problem to make two multiplication facts. Look at the one that has been done already.

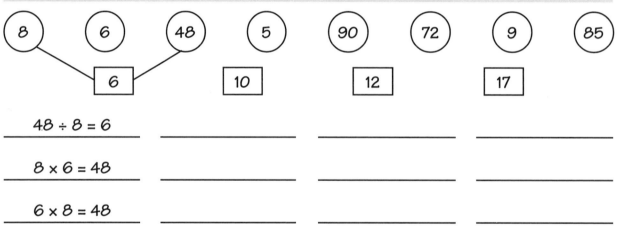

$48 \div 8 = 6$ _____

$8 \times 6 = 48$ _____

$6 \times 8 = 48$ _____

3. In the right-hand box, write two division facts using all three numbers from the left-hand box.

In the right-hand box, write two multiplication facts using all three numbers from the left-hand box.

a.

12, 6, 72	$72 \div 6 = 12$, $72 \div 12 = 6$
60, 10, 6	
5, 13, 65	
36, 9, 4	

b.

54, 6, 9	$6 \times 9 = 54$, $9 \times 6 = 54$
4, 72, 18	
95, 5, 19	
15, 90, 6	

Write out the four related multiplication and division facts for the 15 times table. Like this. $1 \times 15 = 15$, $15 \times 1 = 15$, $15 \div 1 = 15$, $15 \div 15 = 1$. Go as far as 20×15. Try with 13 and 14.

DOUBLES, HALVES, QUARTERS AND EIGHTHS

1. Double each number on the left and then double that answer. One has been done.

a.

8	16	32
7		
9		

40		
90		
70		

$6\frac{1}{2}$		
$4\frac{1}{2}$		
$9\frac{1}{2}$		

$21\frac{1}{2}$		
$17\frac{1}{2}$		
$24\frac{1}{2}$		

Halve the first number and then halve that answer. One has been done.

b.

96	48	24
84		
72		

66		
58		
50		

300		
700		
500		

170		
130		
190		

2. In your head, find a quarter of each number by first finding a half and then halving your answer. Like this: $1600 \div 2 = 800$ $800 \div 2 = 400$ so $400 = \frac{1}{4}$ of 1600.

a.   140 _____   180 _____   160 _____   1000 _____   2000 _____

Find an eighth of these numbers by halving, halving and halving again. Like this: $1200 \div 2 = 600, 600 \div 2 = 300, 300 \div 2 = 150$ so $150 = \frac{1}{8}$ of 1200.

b.   800 _____   208 _____   2400 _____   3600 _____   96 _____

3. You can also find $\frac{1}{4}$ of an amount by dividing by 4 or $\frac{1}{8}$ of an amount by dividing by 8. First write down $\frac{1}{4}$ of each measure. In the second space, record $\frac{3}{4}$ of the amount.

a.   84kg _____ _____   c.   68m _____ _____   e.   80cm _____ _____

b.   96km _____ _____   d.   52p _____ _____   f.   640m _____ _____

In the first space, write down $\frac{1}{8}$ of each measure. In the second space, record $\frac{5}{8}$ of the amount.

g.   56mm _____   _____   i.   88 secs _____   _____

h.   96 mins _____   _____   j.   104 hrs _____   _____

Make a list of some three-digit odd numbers and then both double and halve them. What happens when you halve an odd number? Try halving your answer again!

PARTITIONING WHEN MULTIPLYING

1. This example shows a method of *thinking* that will help you with the calculations on this sheet.

$$43 \times 7 = (40 \times 7) + (3 \times 7) = 280 + 21 = 301$$

Do these problems. Write out all the *thinking stages* in the same way as the example.

a. $96 \times 5 =$ _____

b. $8 \times 58 =$ _____

c. $83 \times 6 =$ _____

d. $9 \times 74 =$ _____

e. $87 \times 4 =$ _____

2. Try to *think* in the same way as you work out the answers to the following calculations.

a.	2	×	64cm	=	128cm	**f.**	43ml	×	8	=	
b.	56m	×	7	=		**g.**	5	×	£47	=	
c.	9	×	37km	=		**h.**	98mm	×	3	=	
d.	79g	×	5	=		**i.**	6	×	61kg	=	
e.	4	×	82p	=		**j.**	25m	×	7	=	

3. Keep *thinking* in the same way as you do these problems.

a. Give the number that is five times the size of eighty-six. _____

b. What is the cost of five items at 68p each? _____

c. Work out the distance round a square with a side of 8.4 metres. _____

d. Bread is priced at £0.94 per loaf. Find the cost of 3 loaves. _____

e. If a train averages 57mph how far will it travel in three hours? _____

Write out your thinking stages for the problems in part 2. Use the example at the top of the page to help you.

P

QUICK MENTAL MATHS

DIVISION WITH REMAINDERS

1. Fill in these division charts. Write the remainder as both a whole number and a fraction as shown.

÷	26	53	64	107
5	5			
r	1			
r	$\frac{1}{5}$			
7				15
r				2
r				$\frac{2}{7}$

÷	29	40	79	113
3				37
r				2
r				$\frac{2}{3}$
9	3			
r	2			
r	$\frac{2}{9}$			

2. Give the answers to the calculations as both a whole number and a decimal. Some answers have been done already.

a. 143 ÷ 2 = | 71 | r | 1 | or | 71.5 |

b. 482 ÷ 4 = | | r | | or | |

c. 843 ÷ 4 = | 210 | r | 3 | or | 210.75 |

d. 285 ÷ 2 = | | r | | or | |

e. 589 ÷ 2 = | | r | | or | |

f. 493 ÷ 4 = | | r | | or | |

g. 463 ÷ 10 = | 46 | r | 3 | or | 46.3 |

h. 529 ÷ 10 = | | r | | or | |

i. 793 ÷ 100 = | 7 | r | 93 | or | 7.93 |

j. 508 ÷ 100 = | | r | | or | |

3. Read these questions carefully and then work them out.

a. There are 47 children on a trip. How many groups of three children can be made?

_____   How many children will be left over? _____

b. How many packets of biscuits can be bought with £10.00 if each packet costs

£0.90? _____   What amount of money will be left over? _____

Divide some three-digit numbers by 6 and by 8. Make sure they are not multiples of the number you are dividing by. Show the remainders as fractions in their lowest terms.

QUICK MENTAL MATHS

CALCULATION PATTERNS (× AND ÷)

1. Fill in the numbers in these multiplication patterns and then complete the sentences.

a.	40	80	120						360	
b.	80		240			480	560			
c.	30				150	180				
d.	60							480		600
e.	50		150	200					450	
f.	100	200					700	800		

g. To find the answers to the x50 table multiply by _____ and then halve.

h. The answers to the x30 table facts are half those of the _____ facts.

i. To multiply by _____ multiply by 100 and then double.

j. The answers to the _____ table facts are half those of the x80 facts.

k. To find the _____ table facts double the x40 facts.

2. Try to work out the pattern of numbers in these halving chains.

(64) → ( ) → (16) → ( ) → ( ) → ( ) → (1)

(192) → ( ) → ( ) → ( ) → ( ) → ( ) → (3)

(320) → ( ) → ( ) → ( ) → ( ) → ( ) → (5)

(10 000) → ( ) → ( ) → ( ) → (625)

3. Complete this division sequence.

4800 ÷ 10 = _____   4800 ÷ 100 = _____   4800 ÷ 1000 = _____

Make up some halving chains of your own like those in part 2. Try doing them in reverse by starting with a number and doubling it over and over. See how many links you can make.

FACTORS AND MULTIPLYING BY 10, 100 AND 1000

1. Write down as many pairs of factors as you can think of for each of these numbers.

a. 36 _____   **e.** 68 _____

b. 48 _____   **f.** 92 _____

c. 80 _____   **g.** 70 _____

d. 44 _____   **h.** 72 _____

Write down five numbers that only have themselves and 1 as factors: **i.** _____

2. This example shows a method of using factors to help you with multiplication.

$$14 \times 12 = 14 \times 3 \times 2 \times 2 = 42 \times 2 \times 2 = 84 \times 2 = 168$$

Do these multiplications and write out all the helping stages in the same way as the example above.

a. 15×8 = _____

b. 19×12 = _____

c. 22×16 = _____

d. 23×12 = _____

3. Make each amount 10, 100 and 1000 times larger.

		× 10	× 100	× 1000
a.	£35		£3500	
b.	12.5m			12 500m
c.	$6\frac{1}{2}$ km			
d.	3.45g		345g	
e.	$6\frac{1}{4}$ kg			6250kg

		×10	×100	×1000
f.	4.02g		402g	
g.	$6\frac{3}{4}$m	67.5m		
h.	£0.05			£50.00
i.	0.020g		2g	
j.	$2\frac{1}{2}$km			2500km

Make a list of the factors for all numbers between 50 and 100. You've already done some of them in part 1. Add these to your list. Do not include numbers with only themselves and 1 as factors.

DIVIDING BY 10, 100, 1000

1. Underneath each abacus write in figures the number that is 10 times smaller than the amount shown.

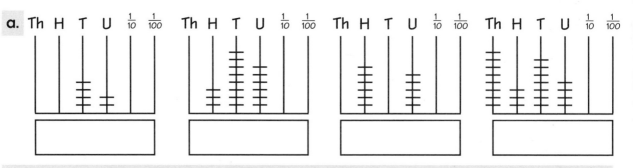

a. Th H T U $\frac{1}{10}$ $\frac{1}{100}$ Th H T U $\frac{1}{10}$ $\frac{1}{100}$ Th H T U $\frac{1}{10}$ $\frac{1}{100}$ Th H T U $\frac{1}{10}$ $\frac{1}{100}$

Now, on the abacuses below, show the number that is 10 times smaller again than the figure you have just written.

b. Th H T U $\frac{1}{10}$ $\frac{1}{100}$ Th H T U $\frac{1}{10}$ $\frac{1}{100}$ Th H T U $\frac{1}{10}$ $\frac{1}{100}$ Th H T U $\frac{1}{10}$ $\frac{1}{100}$

2. Work out these mm lengths and then change the answers first into cm and then into m as shown.

a.	620mm × 2 =	1240mm	124cm	1.24m
b.	6840mm ÷ 2 =	mm	cm	m
c.	2 × 805mm =	mm	cm	m
d.	2440mm ÷ 4 =	mm	cm	m

3. Answer these problems carefully.

a. How many times smaller is 32 than three thousand two hundred?   _____

b. Nine pence multiplied by five is _____ times smaller than £4.50.

c. Plastic cups cost £2.50 per 100. Work out the price of 10 cups.   _____

Draw some eight stick abacuses and show large numbers with up to three decimal places. Test a friend by asking him or her to make the amounts you have shown 10, 100 or 1000 times smaller.

USING RELATED × AND ÷ FACTS

1. Difficult maths problems can sometimes be made easier by doubling one number in the calculation and then halving the result. Look at this example: 16×5, $16 \times 10 = 160$, $160 \div 2 = 80$.

Do these multiplications by writing them out in the same way as the example above.

a. $4 \times 45 =$ _____

b. $25 \times 8 =$ _____

c. $6 \times 45 =$ _____

d. $15 \times 8 =$ _____

e. $35 \times 9 =$ _____

f. $7 \times 15 \ =$ _____

g. $25 \times 9 =$ _____

h. $7 \times 55 =$ _____

Another way to do more difficult multiplication is to halve one number and then double the answer. Like this: 20×15, $10 \times 15 = 150$, $150 \times 2 = 300$.

Now do these multiplications by writing them out in the same way as the example above.

i. $15 \times 12 \ =$ _____

j. $20 \times 16 =$ _____

k. $25 \times 14 =$ _____

l. $21 \times 16 =$ _____

2. Do these multiplications mentally by first multiplying by 100 and then halving the result.

74×50	=	7400	÷	2	=	3700
38×50	=		÷	2	=	
56×50	=		÷	2	=	

63×50	=		÷	2	=	
89×50	=		÷	2	=	
45×50	=		÷	2	=	

3. You can work out the 12, 14, 16, 18 and 20 times table facts by halving and doubling. Like this: 8×14, $8 \times 7 = 56$, $56 \times 2 = 112$

Think in the same way as the examples above to work out the multiplications below.

a. $9 \times 12 =$ _____

b. $14 \times 6 =$ _____

c. $8 \times 18 =$ _____

d. $12 \times 7 =$ _____

e. $16 \times 7 =$ _____

f. $8 \times 16 =$ _____

Multiply some more two-digit numbers by 50 using the same strategy as the one in part 2. Can you work out a similar method for multiplying by 500? If so, try it out.

P

QUICK MENTAL MATHS

PLACE VALUE WHEN MULTIPLYING AND DIVIDING

1. Calculate the answers to these number sentences. Be careful where you place the decimal point.

a. 0.8×6 = _____

b. $3.2 \div 4$ = _____

c. 4×0.6 = _____

d. $0.30 \div 5$ = _____

e. 7×0.05 = _____

f. $6.3 \div 9$ = _____

g. $35 \div 0.7$ = _____

h. 0.8×0.1 = _____

i. $4.0 \div 8$ = _____

j. 4×0.06 = _____

k. $0.35 \div 5$ = _____

l. 0.5×6 = _____

m. 9×0.04 = _____

n. $0.56 \div 7$ = _____

o. 0.07×3 = _____

2. Multiply each number by 2. Write the answers in the first column. In the second column, rearrange the answers according to size with the smallest at the top.

a.	$2 \times 0.57g$	1.14g	
b.	$7.5g \times 2$		
c.	$2 \times 57g$		
d.	$0.75g \times 2$		
e.	$2 \times 5.7g$		

Divide each number by 3. Write the answers in the first column. In the second column, rearrange the answers according to size with the largest at the top.

f.	$2.4m \div 3$		
g.	$42m \div 3$		
h.	$0.42m \div 3$		
i.	$0.24m \div 3$		
j.	$4.2m \div 3$		

3. Write down the answer to the problem first, followed by the value of the 4 in the answer.

a. On a school trip each coach held forty-nine children. There were 7 coaches. How many children were there altogether? _____ _____

b. Eleven groups of fourteen gives a total of _____ _____

c. Divide four thousand six hundred by ten. _____ _____

d. A half of nought point six eight works out at _____ _____

e. Double 0.8, double your answer and then double your answer again. _____ _____

Draw some abacuses to show your answers to part 1. Remember to write underneath each abacus the amount it shows in figures.

×/÷ WHOLE, FRACTIONAL, DECIMAL AND % AMOUNTS

1. Divide these numbers by 6 and then multiply the answer by 8.

a.

18	60	78	36	48	96	24	72	30	84	90	42	66	54
	10						12						
	80										56		

Divide these numbers by 7 and then multiply the answer by 9.

b.

14	49	77	35	63	91	42	21	98	84	28	70	56	105
			5							4			
	63									36			

2. Do the problems below. Be careful where you place the decimal points, and give fractions in their lowest terms.

a. $0.6 \times 9 =$ _____

b. $3.6 \div 4 =$ _____

c. $6 \times 0.07 =$ _____

d. $0.40 \div 5 =$ _____

e. $2.1 \times 5 =$ _____

f. $48 \div 0.4 =$ _____

g. $28 \frac{4}{8} \div 4 =$ _____

h. $7 \frac{2}{5} \times 5 =$ _____

i. $24 \frac{3}{4} \div 3 =$ _____

j. $4 \times 6 \frac{3}{8} =$ _____

k. $6 \frac{5}{10} \div 5 =$ _____

l. $6 \times 8 \frac{4}{6} =$ _____

m. $0.5 \times 8 =$ _____

n. $\frac{15}{20} \times 3 =$ _____

o. $\frac{10}{20} \div 5 =$ _____

3. Divide these amounts by 4 and give your answer as a percentage (%) of 50. The first one has been done already.

64	16	32%		80				52				100		

Find 50% of ↓

a. £2.50 × 3 _____

b. 640kg ÷ 8 _____

Find 25% of ↓

c. 400kg ÷ 5 _____

d. 0.60 × 7 _____

Find 75% of ↓

e. £1.50 × 6 _____

f. 80kg ÷ 10 _____

Choose ten imaginary items from your favourite shop and make up a price-list for them. Reduce the price of each item by the following amounts: 10%, 20%, 25%, 50% and 75%.

QUICK MENTAL MATHS

C13

TEST YOUR SKILLS 1 (C1–C6)

C1 Find the product of each of these pairs of numbers.

a. 10, 5 _____   7, 9 _____   7, 8 _____   7, 7 _____

b. 12, 7 _____   8, 6 _____   5, 6 _____   5, 8 _____

C2 Take each pair of numbers and divide the smaller number into the larger number.

a. 9, 45 _____   54, 6 _____   7, 49 _____   10, 90 _____

b. 64, 8 _____   5, 25 _____   40, 8 _____   4, 32 _____

C3 Write down two other multiplication or division facts using the numbers in the left-hand column.

a.	$150 \times 6 = 900$	$6 \times 150 = 900, 900 \div 6 = 150 (900 \div 150 = 6)$
b.	$350 \div 70 = 5$	
c.	$60 \times 80 = 4800$	
d.	$540 \div 9 = 60$	
e.	$4 \times 45 = 180$	

C4 Work out double, half, a quarter and an eighth of each of these amounts as shown.

320	640	160	80	40
96				
560				

240				
1120				
1360				

C5 Do this problem and write out all the *thinking stages* in the same way as the example below.

$53 \times 6 =$ _____

$43 \times 7 = (40 \times 7) + (3 \times 7) = 280 + 21 = 301$

C6 Give the answer to the calculation in the same way as the completed example.

$485 \div 4 =$ | 121 | r | 1 | or | 121.25 $724 \div 8 =$ | | r | | or |

TOTAL

P

QUICK MENTAL MATHS

TEST YOUR SKILLS 2 (C7–C12)

C7 Try to work out the pattern of numbers in these halving chains.

a. (128) → (   ) → (32) → (   ) → (   ) → (4)

b. (192) → (   ) → (   ) → (   ) → (   ) → (6)

☐

C8 Write down as many factors as you can think of for these numbers.

a. 32 _____   c. 50 _____

b. 40 _____   d. 42 _____

☐

Make each amount 10, 100 and 1000 times larger.

e.

	×10	×100	×1000
£27	£270		
14.4m		1440m	

	×10	×100	×1000
2.75g			2750g
$32\frac{1}{2}$ km		3250km	

☐

C9 Answer these two questions carefully.

a. How many times smaller is fifty-six than 5600? _____

b. 45,000m is the same distance as _____ kilometres.

☐

C10 Work out the sums below by *thinking* in the same way as the example.

8 × 14   8 × 7 = 56   56 × 2 = 112

8 × 12 = _____   7 × 14 = _____   16 × 9 = _____   18 × 6 = _____

☐

C11 Be careful where you put the decimal point when you answer these questions.

0.35 ÷ 5 = _____   0.5 × 20 = _____   4.8 ÷ 4 = _____

☐

C12 Fill in the missing values in the following number sentences.

$(63 ÷ 9) × 4 =$ _____ $\frac{1}{2} ÷ 0.25 =$ _____ $\frac{3}{4} =$ _____% = 0._____

☐

☐ TOTAL

THE FOUR RULES OF NUMBER

1. Work out the answers to these calculations. Remember to work out the parts in brackets first.

a. $15p + 8p + 5p = 6p +$ _____

b. $(42g \div 6) + 21g =$ _____ $+ 14g$

c. $10m \times 4 = (48m \div 6) \times$ _____

d. $(24p \div 6) + 5p = 36p \div$ _____

e. $4m \times 2 \times$ _____ $= 38m - 6m$

f. _____ $= (32g \div 4 \div 4) \times 6 \times 3$

g. $15p +$ _____ $= (42p \div 6) + 21p$

h. $60g = (40g - 14g - 6g) \times$ _____

i. _____ $- 9g = 28g + 10g + 8g$

j. $84m \div 7 = ($ _____ $\div 5) + 8m$

k. $(48 \div 4 \div 4) + 13 +$ _____ $= 25$

l. $8p + 27p = (29p - 3p) +$ _____

2. Study the example that has been done for you. It will help you to solve the others.

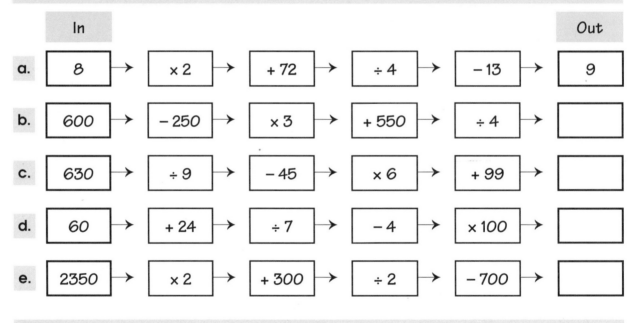

	In					Out
a.	8	× 2	+ 72	÷ 4	− 13	9
b.	600	− 250	× 3	+ 550	÷ 4	
c.	630	÷ 9	− 45	× 6	+ 99	
d.	60	+ 24	÷ 7	− 4	× 100	
e.	2350	× 2	+ 300	÷ 2	− 700	

3. Read these questions and write the answers.

a. Divide sixty by four and multiply the answer by five. _____

b. After spending £7.25, which three coins are given in change from £8? _____

Make up some of your own In/Out machines like those in part 2. Don't forget to use all four signs. Try to make up some longer sums with more operations between the In and Out numbers.

THE FOUR RULES OF NUMBER

1. Work out the answers to these calculations. Remember to do the parts in brackets first.

a. $(60p \div 10) \times 6 = 3 \times$ _____

b. $26m +$ _____ $= 41m - 3m - 5m$

c. $(8 \times 5g) - 7g - 8g -$ _____ $= 21g$

d. $(22g \div 2) + 15g =$ _____ $+ 6g$

e. $5m \times 4 = 5m \times 2 \times$ _____

f. $(42p \div 6) -$ _____ $= 24p \div 4$

g. $37g = (36g \div 6) + 3g + 37g -$ _____

h. _____ $\div 5 = (28p \div 4) - 3p$

i. $37p + 6p -$ _____ $= 12p + 23p$

j. $3 \times £3 = (9 \times £7) \div$ _____

k. $40m \div 5 = (25m \div 5) +$ _____

l. $6g \times 7 = 51g - 5g -$ _____

2. Multiply the two numbers in the first box together, add 1000, halve that answer and then subtract 110. Good luck!

a.	4, 7	28	1028	514	404
b.	8, 5	40			
c.	6, 9		1054		
d.	18, 4			536	
e.	5, 16				430

f.	8, 12		1096		
g.	3, 6			509	
h.	9, 30				525
i.	20, 7	140			
j.	5, 50		1250		

2. Read these questions and work out the answers.

a. From the product of nine and nine subtract the sum of nine and nine. _____

b. Work out $\frac{1}{6}$ of 30 and multiply the answer by 2000. _____

c. Divide a third of ninety-six by a half of 8 and add 5 to the answer. _____

d. Subtract twenty-two from fifty and then halve your answer. _____

Choose other pairs of numbers like those in part 2 above. Carry out the same steps. Then try a different sequence of instructions.

THE FOUR RULES OF NUMBER

1. Double the amount in the left-hand box, add 150, divide that answer by 4 and then subtract 30. The first one has been done for you.

a.				
29cm	58cm	208cm	52cm	22cm

b.				
11m				13m

c.				
19km			47km	

d.				
37g		224g		

e.				
21kg	42kg			

f.				
55p			65p	

g.				
£73	£146			

h.				
49kg		248kg		

i.				
85g			80g	

j.				
61km				38km

2. Using the +, −, ×, ÷ and = signs make up ten sums that all have at least four different signs in them. Like this: $(18 + 12) - 20 = 5 \times (30 \div 15)$ The signs can be in any order. You will need to use brackets.

a. _____   f. _____

b. _____   g. _____

c. _____   h. _____

d. _____   i. _____

e. _____   j. _____

3. Solve the problems below. Read each question carefully and think before you start!

a. Tim's marbles equal $\frac{1}{4}$ of 36. Janine's marbles equal $\frac{1}{3}$ of 30.

   Who has the most marbles and by how many? _____

b. A purse held 5 FIVES and 4 TWENTIES. How much less than £2 was this? _____

c. Find the product of 2, 3, 12 and 2. _____

 Using the +, −, ×, ÷ and = signs make up ten more sums with brackets like those in part 2.

THE FOUR RULES OF NUMBER

1. Study the example that has been done for you. It will help you to solve the others.

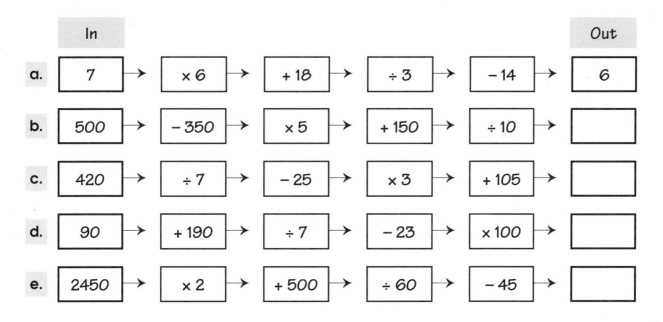

	In					Out
a.	7	× 6	+ 18	÷ 3	− 14	6
b.	500	− 350	× 5	+ 150	÷ 10	
c.	420	÷ 7	− 25	× 3	+ 105	
d.	90	+ 190	÷ 7	− 23	× 100	
e.	2450	× 2	+ 500	÷ 60	− 45	

2. Read these questions and work out the answers.

a. Share the sum of thirty-eight, fifty-two and ten by four. _____

b. Ros has four FIVES, six TENS and five TWENTIES.
How much does she still need to save to buy a book costing £5.00? _____

c. Write the number that is eight times greater than six times five. _____

3. Multiply the two numbers in the first box together, add 2000, halve that answer and then subtract 101. Good luck!

a.	6, 4	24	2024	1012	911
b.	4, 8	32			
c.	8, 9		2072		
d.	8, 30			1120	

e.	30, 6		2180		
f.	4, 40			1080	
g.	8, 8				931
h.	20, 7	140			

Choose other pairs of numbers like those in part 3 above. Carry out the same steps. You could then try a different sequence of instructions.

A1

1.
a. **13**, 21, 29, **37**, **45**, 53, 61, 69, **77**
b. – 18, **– 9**, 0, 9, 18, 27, **36**, **45**, 54
c. 12.2, **12.8**, 13.4, 14, 14.6, **15.2**, 15.8, 16.4, **17**

2.
a. **1025**, 1015, 1005, 995, 985, 975, 965, 955, 945, **935**
b. **21 017**, 21 007, 20 997, 20 987, 20 977, 20 967, 20 957, 20 947, 20 937
c. **5756**, 5856, 5956, 6056, 6156, 6256, 6356, 6456, 6556, **6656**
d. **45 409**, 45 509, 45 609, 45 709, 45 809, 45 909, 46 009, 46 109, **46 209**

3. The following numbers in the square should be shaded:
a. 4, 11, 18, 25, 32, 39, 46, 53, 60
b. 67, 74, 81, 88, 95, 102, 109
c. 5 ¼, 6 ½, 7 ¾ d. 10 ½, 9, 7 ½

A2

1. a. 43 b. 278 c. 5961 d. 21 683 e. 457 932 f. 608 g. 7019
h. 5006 i. 3800 j. 10 002 k. 80 088 l. 88 008

2. a. one hundred and five b. one hundred and fifty
c. eight thousand and six d. eight thousand and sixty e. eight
thousand six hundred f. six thousand and eight g. twenty-four
thousand, nine hundred and seventy
h. 4 = 400 000, 7 = 70 000, 2 = 2000, 9 = 900, 3 = 30, 5 = 5

3. a. 0.5, 0.25, 0.27, 0.5, 0.8
b. 0.25, 0.5, 0.5, 0.75, 0.2
c. 0.3, 0.7, 0.9, 0.4, 0.75

A3

1. Accept a 4 or 5-digit number: a. greater than £3162
b. less than £49 074 c. less than £1030 d. greater than
£58 000 e. greater than £2653
Accept a fraction: f. less than ⅔ g. greater than ¾
h. greater than ⅔ i. less than 7/10 j. less than ⅛
Accept a decimal fraction to 1 or 2 decimal places: k. less
than 43.2cm l. less than 59.95km m. greater than 69.9kg
n. greater than 8.57mm o. less than 0.65ml

2. a. 98 347, 97 834, 94 783, 93 478, 84 793, 83 947, 83 794, 83 497
b. – 100, – 83, – 79, – 1, 1, 79, 83, 100, 101, 110, 1100
These numbers should be circled: c. ⅔ d. 0.8 e. 0.75 f. ¼
g. 0.16 h. ½

3. a. 70% b. 40% c. 25% d. 50% e. 75%

A4

1. a. 175, 170cm b. 125, 130ml c. 550, 560 hours
d. 75, 80km e. 160, 150m f. 2500, 2400mm g. 100, 110kg
h. 900, £880 i. 350, 330p j. 5500, 5400 min

2. a. 1000, 2500, 4000, 5500, 7000, 8500
b. 500, 1250, 2000, 2750, 3500, 4250
c. 3.21, 3.22, 3.23, 3.24, 3.25, **3.26**, 3.27, 3.28, 3.29

3. Open-ended – numbers should be between:
a. 1400 and 1600 b. 6000 and 6500 c. 350 and 400
d. 22 000 and 23 000

A5

1. a. 50m, 1010m, 550m, 29 640m
b. 700km, 4000km, 48 400km, 679 900km
c. 1000 miles, 27 000 miles, 7000 miles, 39 000 miles

2. a. 156, 160 b. 112, 110 c. 48, 50 d. 14, 10 e. 49, 50 f. 45, 50
g. 41, 40 h. 81, 80 i. 118, 120 j. 154, 150 k. 75, 80 l. 42, 40

3. a. 3, 98, 109 b. 7, 46, 316 c. 8, 38, 273 d. 5, 22, 521
e. £4.90 f. 3.30m

A6

A1. a. 1, 14, **27**, **40**, 53, 66, 79, 92
b. 150, **135**, 120, **105**, **90**, 75, 60, 45
c. 14.1, 14.9, **15.7**, ·16.5, **17.3**, **18.1**, 18.9, 19.7
d. **– 16**, – 9, **– 2**, **5**, 12, 19, 26, 33
e. 8.25, 8.19, 8.13, **8.07**, 8.01, **7.95**, **7.89**, 7.83
f. **24 ½**, 21, 17 ½, 14, 10 ½, 7, **3 ½**, 0

A2. a. 426 135.78
b. 5 = 500 000, 9 = 90 000, 6 = 6000, 2 = 200, 4 = 40, 3 = 3
c. 0.4, 0.6, 0.25, 0.75

A3.

– 98ºC	£43 709	0.18
– 79ºC	£43 790	25%
– 49ºC	£43 897	50%
49ºC	£43 907	0.7
78ºC	£43 970	¾
97ºC	£43 987	⅘

A7

A4. a. 200, 190cm b. 550, 540ml c. 300, 310m d. 75, 70km
e. 20, 17 ½ f. 10, 11 g. 5, 5.1 h. 1.5, 1.6
i. 11 000, 12 500, 14 000, 15 500, 17 000
j. 3500, 4250, 5000, 5750, 6500

A5. a. **560, 600, 1000** b. 9780, 9800, 10 000 c. 4500, 4500, 4000
d. 640, 600, 1000 e. 8570, 8600, 9000 f. 3010, 3000, 3000
g. 6930, 6900, 7000 h. 7990, 8000, 8000
i. 6, 2, 4, 6, 10 j. 3, 9, 7, 42, 21

B1

1. **a.** £70 **b.** 50cm **c.** 71kg **d.** 1000mm **e.** 670km **f.** 27cm
g. 800ml **h.** 230g **i.** £780 **j.** 700m **k.** 500kg **l.** 565mm

2. **a.** 100 **b.** 92 **c.** 100 **d.** 90 **e.** 300 **f.** 81 **g.** 92 **h.** 100 **i.** 100 **j.** 100
k. 63 **l.** 300

m.

600	900	**300**	700	400
900	1200	600	1000	**700**
1200	1500	900	1300	1000
1400	1700	1100	**1500**	1200

3. **a.** 200 **b.** 3000 **c.** 790cm, 7m, 90cm

B2

1. **a.** 50 **b.** 80 **c.** 290 **d.** 160 **e.** 180 **f.** 190
g. 2687 **h.** 9521 **i.** 7612 **j.** 6456 **k.** 6656 **l.** 4609

m.

626	454	**733**	545	332
446	274	553	365	**152**
736	564	843	**655**	442
516	**344**	623	435	222

2. **a.** 110ml **b.** 700m **c.** 140cm **d.** 800km **e.** 120mm **f.** 500cm
g. 900m **h.** £90 **i.** 1400g **j.** 140ml **k.** 1500km **l.** 50mm

3. **a.** eight hundred **b.** five hundred and thirty-six **c.** one hundred
and sixty-two **d.** one hundred and eighty-two **e.** two hundred
and forty-six

B3

1. **a.** (completed example – sums in any order)
b. 64: 64 + 43, 43 + 64, 107 – 64
c. 280: 224 + 56, 280 – 56, 280 – 224
d. 658: 27 + 658, 658 + 27, 685 – 658
e. 807: 49 + 758, 807 – 758, 807 – 49

2. (185: 48, 137) (93: 57, 36) (782: 325, 457)
48 + 137 = 185, 57 + 36 = 93, 325 + 457 = 782
185 – 137 = 48, 93 – 36 = 57, 782 – 457 = 325
185 – 48 = 137, 93 – 57 = 36, 782 – 325 = 457

3. **a.** These addition facts with numbers in any order:
(72 + 180 = 252) (160 + 53 = 213) (490 + 320 = 810)
(370 + 67 = 437)
b. Subtraction facts using the three numbers given: (870, 490,
380) (7389, 500, 6889) (1600, 900, 700) (685, 360, 325)

B4

1. **a.** 26, 14, 2, 27, 32, 24
b. 11, 25, 16, 38, 13, 23
c. 44, 27, 78, 94, 57, 83
d. 39, 22, 36, 72, 51, 65

2.
a. £6.50	**b.** 14.3m	**c.** 1250p
£15.20	11.5m	1310p
£10.50	11.4m	1540p
£16.20	11.5m	1600p

3.

31	62	124		48	96	192		39	78	156		26	52	104
46	92	184		27	54	108		21	42	84		13	26	52
17	34	68		16	32	64		49	98	196		45	90	180
37	74	148		42	84	168		15	30	60		18	36	72
24	48	96		23	46	92		28	56	112		36	72	144
12	24	48		35	70	140		19	38	76		14	28	56

B5

1. **a.** 160 **b.** 540 **c.** 520 **d.** 790 **e.** 410 **f.** 160 **g.** 630 **h.** 760
i. 280 **j.** 390 **k.** 670 **l.** 900

2. **a.** 190g **b.** 77

3. Open-ended – eight addition sums each with three numbers
using all the numbers given. (Check that the largest number is
first in each sum.)

B6

1. **a.** 710 **b.** 1170 **c.** 1820 **d.** 830 **e.** 580 **f.** 320 **g.** 860 **h.** 600
i. 1590 **j.** 1895 **k.** 1080 **l.** 480

2. £500 + £500 – £30 – £10 = £960
600m + 600m + 10m + 20m = 1230m
800g + 800g + 100g or 900g + 900g – 100g = 1700g

3. **a.** one hundred and seventy-eight **b.** one thousand two
hundred and thirty-four **c.** two hundred and seven

B7

1. **a.** 64, 90, 256, 74 **b.** 74, 74, 402, 84 **c.** 8, 36, 406, 42
d. 107, 65, 525, 99 **e.** 71, 71, 615, 99 **f.** 32, 64, 738, 48
g. 160, 258, 374 **h.** 465, 553, 643

2. **a.** E + E + E = EVEN **b.** O + O = EVEN **c.** O + O + O = ODD
d. E + E = EVEN **e.** E + O = ODD **f.** O + E = ODD
g. O – O = EVEN **h.** E – E = EVEN

3. **a.** 135, 145, 155, 165
b. 8, 18, 28, 38

B8

1. **a.** 550 + 40 + 8 + 6 = 590 + 14 = 604
b. 30 + 750 + 7 + 5 = 780 + 12 = 792
c. 642 + 8 + 21 = 650 + 21 = 671
d. 913, 285, 431

2.

434	+	**242**			234	+	725		
=	400	+	200		=	**200**	+	700	
+	30	+	40		+	30	+	**20**	
+	4	+	2		+	**4**	+	5	
=	600	+	70	+ 6	=	900	+	50	+ 9
=	676				=	**959**			

3. **a.** 699 **b.** 604

B9

1.
a. $62 + 60 - 4 = 118$
b. $94 + 90 - 3 = 181$
c. $83 + 80 - 2 = 161$
d. $82 + 100 - 1 = 181$

2.
a. $157 + 20 - 1 = 176$
b. $385 - 70 + 1 = 316$
c. $537 + 40 + 1 - 578$
d. $542 - 20 - 1 = 521$
e. $246 + 40 - 1 = 285$

3.
a. 375g

B10

1. a. £620.00 b. 440km c. 2887 miles d. 1626kg e. 380g
f. 1582 litres g. 1900m h. 2000km i. 543kg j. 999 miles
k. £640 l. 138 litres m. 853km n. 951g

2.

$\frac{1}{2}$	**0.5**	**50%**		$\frac{1}{100}$	0.01	**1%**		$\frac{9}{10}$	**0.9**	90%		$\frac{1}{10}$	0.1	**10%**
$\frac{3}{5}$	0.6	60%		$\frac{49}{100}$	**0.49**	49%		$\frac{3}{4}$	0.75	75%		$\frac{9}{100}$	0.09	**9%**
$\frac{17}{100}$	**0.17**	17%		$\frac{4}{5}$	0.8	80%		$\frac{91}{100}$	0.91	**91%**		$\frac{1}{5}$	**0.2**	20%
$\frac{7}{10}$	0.7	**70%**		$\frac{1}{4}$	**0.25**	25%		$\frac{2}{5}$	0.4	**40%**		$\frac{3}{10}$	0.3	30%

3. a. 4 b. 4 c. 1 d. 4 e. 6 f. 2 g. 2 h. 3 i. 8 j. 4

B11

1. The first answer for each question should be connected
with a pencil line to the second answer which is given
in words on the question sheet.
a. 688 – six hundred and eighty-eight b. 691 – six hundred
and ninety-one c. 4304 – four thousand, three hundred and
four d. 1072 – one thousand and seventy-two e. 61591 – sixty
one thousand, five hundred and ninety-one f. 24150 – twenty
four thousand, one hundred and fifty

2. a. 457cm, 7cm b. 375ml, 70ml c. 766mm, 700mm d. 970p 70p
e. 730cm, 700cm f. 6.73m, 7/10(70cm) g. 7145m, 7000m
h. 1276km, 70km i. 7995g, 7000g j. £4754, £700

3. a. 38 b. 24 c. five thousand two hundred d. 2002 thousands
e. 52, 493

B12

1. a. 200 b. 240 c. 250 d. 210 e. 280 f. 206
g. Depending on the numbers chosen to subtract, any
one of these three answers would be acceptable:
Column 1: 650, 660, 630
Column 2: 500, 510, 480
Column 3: 750, 760, 730
Column 4: 600, 610, 580
Column 5: 50, 60, 30
Column 6: 300, 310, 280
Column 7: 150, 160, 130
Column 8: 100, 110, 80
Column 9: 350, 360, 330

2. a. 270cm b. 349km c. 59 d. 716 e. 135

3. a. 90 b. 6 c. 24 d. 27 e. 22 f. 20

B13

B1. a. 110 b. 100 c. 54 d. 93 e. 1200 f. 759 g. 760 h. 899
i. 910 j. 200 k. 690 l. 210

B2.

255	664	143	471		170	460	380	290
125	534	**13**	341		**40**	330	250	160

B3. The four facts can be in any order:
a. $256 + 45 = 301$, $45 + 256 = 301$
$301 - 256 = 45$, $301 - 45 = 256$
b. $800 + 480 = 1280$, $480 + 800 = 1280$
$1280 - 800 = 480$, $1280 - 480 = 800$

B4. **26, 76**   33, 83   18, 68   4, 54

B5. Open-ended – four addition sums using all the numbers given.
(Check that the largest number has been written first.)

B6. double 500 minus 1 = 999; double 800 minus 13 = 1587

B14

B7. a. odd b. even c. odd d. odd e. even f. even g. odd
h. even i. even

B8. a. $457 + 42 = 450 + 40 + 7 + 2 = 490 + 9 = 499$

B9. a. $93 + 70 - 2 = 161$ b. $72 + 90 - 1 = 161$ c. $64 + 60 - 3 = 121$
d. $428 - 60 + 2 = 370$ e. $249 - 90 + 4 = 163$ f. $337 - 50 + 3 = 290$

B10.

$\frac{1}{100}$	0.01	1%		$\frac{1}{10}$	0.1	**10%**		$\frac{1}{5}$	**0.2**	20%
$\frac{1}{4}$	**0.25**	25%		$\frac{1}{2}$	0.5	50%		$\frac{3}{4}$	0.75	**75%**

g. 440km h. 1742kg

B11. $4 = 400\,000$ $7 = 70\,000$ $3 = 3000$
$9 = 900$ $5 = 50$ $6 = 6$

B12. a. 26 b. 85

C1

1. a. £48 b. 7 c. 9 d. 80mm e. 5 f. 7 g. 70ml h. 7 i. 6
j. 49m k. 7 l. 6

2. a. 56, 64, 21 b. 20, 30, 72 c. 90, 35, 54 d. 48, 81, 24
e. 36, 70, 60 f. 54, 36, 56

55p	70p	60p	75p	**65p**
33p	42p	36p	**45p**	39p
66p	84p	**72p**	90p	78p
44p	**56p**	48p	60p	52p

3. a. 75 b. 84 drinks c. 78 d. 96p

C2

1. a. 8, 5, 6 b. 7, 10, 9 c. 11, 7, 4 d. 6, 8, 5 e. 3, 5, 5
f. 5, 10, 7

g.

£14	£16	**£22**	£18	£24
£7	**£8**	£11	£9	£12

14cm	12cm	**11cm**	15cm	13cm

2. a. 6ml b. 6 c. 70cm d. 6km e. 45mm f. 4 g. 12m h. 10 i. 72g
j. 9ml k. 32km l. 6

3. a. eleven b. eighteen each c. nineteen d. four
e. sixteen centimetres

C3

1. a. (completed example – sums in any order)
   b. 84, 12 × 7 = 84, 84 ÷ 7 = 12, 84 ÷ 12 = 7
   c. 8, 48 ÷ 8 = 6, 6 × 8 = 48, 8 × 6 = 48
   d. 6, 54 ÷ 6 = 9, 9 × 6 = 54, 6 × 9 = 54
   e. 70, 14 × 5 = 70, 70 ÷ 5 = 14, 70 ÷ 14 = 5

2. (10: 90, 9)   (12: 72, 6)   (17: 85, 5)
   90 ÷ 9 = 10   72 ÷ 6 = 12   85 ÷ 5 = 17
   9 × 10 – 90   6 × 12 = 72   5 × 17 = 85
   10 × 9 = 90   12 × 6 = 72   17 × 5 = 85

3. a. 72 ÷ 6 = 12, 72 ÷ 12 = 6   b. 6 × 9 = 54, 9 × 6 = 54

60 ÷ 6 = 10, 60 ÷ 10 = 6	4 × 18 = 72, 18 × 4 = 72
65 ÷ 5 = 13, 65 ÷ 13 = 5	5 × 19 = 95, 19 × 5 = 95
36 ÷ 9 = 4, 36 ÷ 4 = 9	6 × 15 = 90, 15 × 6 = 90

C4

1.
16	32
14	28
18	36

80	160
180	360
140	280

13	26
9	18
19	38

43	86
35	70
49	98

48	24
42	21
36	18

33	16 ½
29	14 ½
25	12 ½

150	75
350	175
250	125

85	42 ½
65	32 ½
95	47 ½

2. a. 35, 45, 40, 250, 500
   b. 100, 26, 300, 450, 12

3. a. 21kg, 63kg b. 24km, 72km c. 17m, 51m d. 13p, 39p
   e. 20cm, 60cm f. 160m, 480m
   g. 7mm, 35mm h. 12 mins, 60 mins i. 11 secs, 55 secs
   j. 13 hrs, 65 hrs

C5

1. a. 95 × 5 = (90 × 5) + (6 × 5) = 450 + 30 = 480
   b. 8 × 58 = (8 × 8) + (50 × 8) = 64 + 400 = 464
   c. 83 × 6 = (80 × 6) + (3 × 6) = 480 + 18 = 498
   d. 9 × 74 = (9 × 4) + (70 × 9) = 36 + 630 = 666
   e. 87 × 4 = (80 × 4) + (7 × 4) = 320 + 28 = 348

2. a. 128cm b. 392m c. 333km d. 395g e. 328p f. 344ml g. £235 h.
   294mm i. 366kg j. 175m

3. a. 430 b. 340p (£3.40) c. 33.6m d. £2.82 e. 171 miles

C6

1.
5	10	12	21
1	3	4	2
1/5	3/5	4/5	2/5

9	13	26	37
2	1	1	2
2/3	1/3	1/3	2/3

3	7	9	15
5	4	1	2
5/7	4/7	1/7	2/7

3	4	8	12
2	4	7	5
2/9	4/9	7/9	5/9

2. a. 71 r 1 or 71.5 b. 120 r 2 or 120.5 c. 210 r 3 or 210.75
   d. 142 r 1 or 142.5 e. 294 r 1 or 294.5 f. 123 r 1 or 123.25
   g. 46 r 3 or 46.3 h. 52 r 9 or 52.9 i. 7 r 93 or 7.93 j. 5 r 8 or 5.08

3. a. 15 groups, 2 children b. 11 packets, 10p

C7

1. a. 40, **80**, **120**, 160, 200, 240, 280, 320, **360**, 400
   b. 80, 160, **240**, 320, 400, **480**, **560**, 640, 720, 800
   c. **30**, 60, 90, 120, **150**, **180**, 210, 240, 270, 300
   d. **60**, 120, 180, 240, 300, 360, 420, **480**, 540, **600**
   e. **50**, 100, **150**, **200**, 250, 300, 350, 400, **450**, 500
   f. **100**, **200**, 300, 400, 500, 600, **700**, **800**, 900, 1000
   g. 100 h. ×60 i. 200 j. ×40 k. ×80

2. 64, 32, **16**, 8, 4, 2, **1**
   192, 96, 48, 24, 12, 6, **3**
   320, 160, 80, 40, 20, 10, **5**
   10 000, 5000, 2500, 1250, **625**

3. 480, 48, 4.8

C8

1. a. **36** (1, 36) (2, 18) (3, 12) (4, 9) (6, 6)
   b. **48** (1, 48) (2, 24) (3,16) (4, 12) (6, 8)
   c. **80** (1, 80) (2, 40) (4, 20) (5, 16) (8, 10)
   d. **44** (1, 44) (2, 22) (4, 11) e. **68** (1, 68) (2, 34) (4, 17)
   f. **92** (1, 92) (2, 46) 4, 23) g. **70** (1, 70) (2, 35) (5 14) (7, 10)
   h. **72** (1, 72) (2, 36) (3, 24) (4, 18) (5, 14) (6, 12) (8, 9)
   i. Open-ended – five numbers with only 1 and themselves as
   factors.

2. a. 15 × 2 × 2 × 2 = 30 × 2 × 2 = 60 × 2 = 120
   b. 19 × 3 × 2 × 2 = 57 × 2 × 2 = 114 × 2 = 228
   c. 22 × 4 × 2 × 2 = 88 × 2 × 2 = 176 × 2 = 352
   d. 23 × 3 × 2 × 2 = 69 × 2 × 2 = 138 × 2 = 276

3. a. £350, **£3500**, £35 000 b. 125m, 1250m, **12 500m** c. 65km, 650km,
   6500km d. 34.5g, **345g**, 3450g e. 62.5kg, 625kg, **6250kg**
   f. 40.2g, **402g**, 4020g g. **67.5m**, 675m 6750m h. £0.50, £5.00,
   £50.00 i. 0.20g, **2g**, 20g j. 25km, 250km, **2500km**

C9

1. a. 4.2, 38.6, 60.5, 837.4
   b. Abacus drawings marked to show the following
   numbers:
   0.42   3.86   6.05   83.74

2. a. 1240mm   124cm   1.24m
   b. 3420mm   342cm   3.42m
   c. 1610mm   161cm   1.61m
   d. 610mm   61cm   0.61m

3. a. 100 b. 10 c. 25p (£0.25)

C10

1. a. 4 × 45   4 × 90 = 360   360 ÷ 2 = 180
   b. 25 × 8   50 × 8 = 400   400 ÷ 2 = 200
   c. 6 × 45   6 × 90 = 540   540 ÷ 2 = 270
   d. 15 × 8   30 × 8 = 240   240 ÷ 2 = 120
   e. 35 × 9   70 × 9 = 630   630 ÷ 2 = 315
   f. 7 × 15   7 × 30 = 210   210 ÷ 2 = 105
   g. 25 × 9   50 × 9 = 450   450 ÷ 2 = 225
   h. 7 × 55   7 × 110 = 770   770 ÷ 2 = 385

   i. 15 × 12   15 × 6 = 90   90 × 2 = 180
   j. 20 × 16   10 × 16 = 160   160 × 2 = 320
   k. 25 × 14   25 × 7 = 175   175 × 2 = 350
   l. 21 × 16   21 × 8 = 168   168 × 2 = 336

2. | 7400 | 3700 | 6300 | 3150 |
   |---|---|---|---|
   | 3800 | 1900 | 8900 | 4450 |
   | 5600 | 2800 | 4500 | 2250 |

3. a. 108 b. 84 c. 144 d. 84 e. 112 f. 128

C11

1. a. 4.8 b. 0.8 c. 2.4 d. 0.06 e. 0.35 f. 0.7 g. 50 h. 0.08 i. 0.5 j. 0.24 k. 0.07 l. 3 m. 0.36 n. 0.08 o. 0.21

2.

a.	2 × 0.57g	**1.14g**	1.14g	f.	**2.4m ÷ 3**	0.8m	14m
b.	7.5g × 2	15g	1.5g	g.	42m ÷ 3	14m	1.4m
c.	2 × 57g	114g	11.4g	h.	0.42m ÷ 3	0.14m	0.8m
d.	0.75g × 2	1.5g	15g	i.	0.24m ÷ 3	0.08m	0.14m
e.	2 × 5.7g	11.4g	114g	j.	4.2m ÷ 3	1.4m	0.08m

3. a. 343, 40 b. 154, 4 c. 460, 400 d. 0.34, $\frac{4}{100}$ e. 6.4, $\frac{4}{10}$

D1

1. a. 22p b. 14g c. 5 d. 4 e. 4 f. 36g g. 13p h. 3 i. 55g j. 20m k. 9 l. 9p

2.
a. **8**   **9**
b. **600**   400
c. **630**   249
d. **60**   800
e. **2350**   1800

3. a. 75 b. 50p, 20p, 5p

C12

1a.

3	**10**	13	6	8	16	4	**12**	5	14	15	7	11	9
24	**80**	104	48	64	128	32	96	40	112	120	**56**	88	72

1b.

2	7	11	**5**	9	13	6	3	14	12	**4**	10	8	15
18	**63**	99	45	81	117	54	27	126	108	**36**	90	72	135

2. a. 5.4 b. 0.9 c. 0.42 d. 0.08 e. 10.5 f. 120 g. $7\frac{1}{8}$ h. 37 i. $8\frac{1}{4}$ j. $25\frac{1}{2}$ k. $1\frac{3}{10}$ l. 52 m. 4 n. $2\frac{1}{4}$ o. $\frac{1}{10}$

3. **80**, 20, 40%
52, 13, 26%
100, 25, 50%
a. £3.75 b. 40kg c. 20kg d. £1.05 e. £6.75 f. 6kg

D2

1. a. 12p b. 7m c. 4g d. 20g e. 2 f. 1p g. 9g h. 20p i. 8p j. 7 k. 3m l. 4g

2.
a. **28** **1028** **514** **404**   f. 96 **1096** 548 438
b. **40** 1040 520 410   g. 18 1018 **509** 399
c. **54** **1054** 527 417   h. 270 1270 635 **525**
d. **72** 1072 **536** 426   i. **140** 1140 570 460
e. **80** 1080 540 **430**   j. 250 **1250** 625 515

3. a. 63 b. 10 000 c. 13 d. 14

C13

C1. a. 50, 63, 56, 49
b. 84, 48, 30, 40
C2. a. 5, 9, 7, 9
b. 8, 5, 5, 8
C3. Two of the following three facts should be shown:
a. (completed example)
b. 350 ÷ 5 = 70, 5 × 70 = 350, 70 × 5 = 350
c. 80 × 60 = 4800, 4800 ÷ 80 = 60, 4800 ÷ 60 = 80
d. 540 ÷ 60 = 9, 9 × 60 = 540, 60 × 9 = 540
e. 45 × 4 = 180, 180 ÷ 45 = 4, 180 ÷ 4 = 45
C4. (completed example)
96, 192, 48, 24, 12
560, 1120, 280, 140, 70
240, 480, 120, 60, 30
1120, 2240, 560, 280, 140
1360, 2720, 680, 340, 170
C5. 53 × 6 = (50 × 6) + (3 × 6) = 300 + 18 = 318
C6. 724 ÷ 8 = 90 r 4 or 90.5

D3

1. a. **29cm** 58cm 208cm 52cm 22cm
b. 11m 22m 172m 43m **13m**
c. **19km** 38km 188km **47km** 17km
d. **37g** 74g **224g** 56g 26g
e. **21kg** 42kg 192kg 48kg 18kg
f. **55p** 110p 260p **65p** 35p
g. **£73** £146 £296 £74 £44
h. 49g 98kg **248kg** 62kg 32kg
i. **85g** 170g 320g **80g** 50g
j. **61km** 122km 272km 68km **38km**

2. Open-ended – ten sums all with at least four different signs in them chosen from +, −, ×, ÷ and =.

3. a. Janine, 1 b. 95p (£0.95) c. 144

C14

C7. a. **128**, 64, **32**, 16, 8, **4**
b. **192**, 96, 48, 24, 12, **6**

C8. a. **32** – 1, 21, 2, 16, 4, 8
b. **40** – 1, 40, 2, 20, 4, 10, 5, 8
c. **50** – 1, 50, 2, 25, 5, 10
d. **42** – 1, 42, 2, 21, 3, 14, 6, 7
e. **£27 – £270**, £2700, **£27 000**
14.4m – 144m, **1440m**, 14 000m
2.75g – 27.5g, 275g, **2750g**
$32\frac{1}{2}$ – 325km, **3250km**, 32 500km

C9. a. 100 b. 45km

C10. 96, 98, 144, 108

C11. 0.07, 10, 1.2

C12. 28, 2, 75%, 0.75

D4

1.
a. **7**   6
b. **500**   90
c. **420**   210
d. **90**   1700
e. **2450**   45

2. a. 25 b. £3.20 c. 240

3.
a. **24** **2024** **1012** **911**
b. **32** 2032 1016 915
c. **72** **2072** 1036 935
d. 240 2240 **1120** 1019
e. 180 **2180** 1090 989
f. 160 2160 **1080** 979
g. 64 2064 1032 **931**
h. **140** 2140 1070 969